MW00845991

MASTERMINDS Riddle Math Series

— Elementary Grades —

WHOLE NUMBERS, ADDITION, SUBTRACTION, MULTIPLICATION, AND DIVISION

Reproducible Skill Builders And Higher Order Thinking Activities Based On NCTM Standards

By Brenda Opie
and Douglas McAvinn

Incentive Publications, Inc.
Nashville, Tennessee

Illustrated by Douglas McAvinn
Cover illustration by Douglas McAvinn

ISBN 978-0-86530-604-2

2   3   4   5   6   7   8   9   10   11   10   09   08

PRINTED IN THE UNITED STATES OF AMERICA
www.incentivepublications.com

TABLE OF CONTENTS

1

What if...

What if cavemen played golf? What if we lived under water and had to swim everywhere? What if there were no numbers in our world? Think of many, varied, and unusual things that might occur if there were no numbers in our world. Try to think of at least five. Two have been done for you.

1. **We wouldn't know how old we are.**

_____

2. **We couldn't count the number of teeth we have in our mouths.**

_____

3. _____

4. _____

5. _____

6. _____

7. _____

8. _____

Discovering uses of numbers   NAME _____

SEARCHING THE WORLD FOR NUMBERS

DIRECTIONS: Put on your thinking cap and think of the many, varied, and unusual places that you find numbers in the "real" world. Try to think of at least eight. Three have been done for you.

1. on a bicycle tire
    _____

2. inside your shoe
    _____

3. on an egg carton
    _____

4. _____   9. _____

5. _____   10. _____

6. _____   11. _____

7. _____   12. _____

8. _____   13. _____

Ordering numbers

NAME _____

From Smallest to Largest

DIRECTIONS: Number from smallest to largest. The first one is done for you.

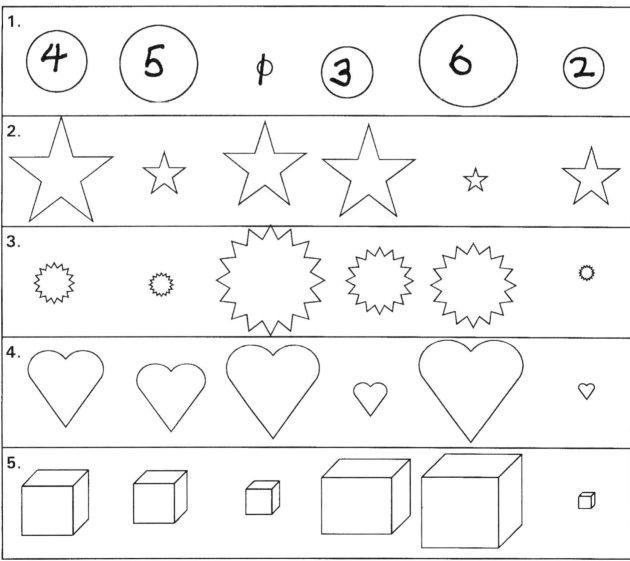

1. 4 5 φ 3 6 2

2.

3.

4.

5.

BONUS: On the back of this paper draw 6 shapes from small to big and write the numbers 1 to 6 in them just like you did in the shapes above.

Adding: Using pictures   NAME _____

Where is a frog's favorite place to prop up her feet?

DIRECTIONS: Count the total number of objects in each set. Find your answer in the secret code. Write the letter of the problem above it.

1.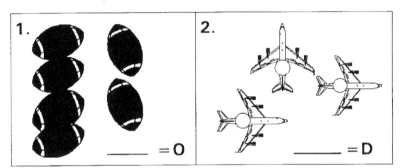
_____ = O

2.
_____ = D

3.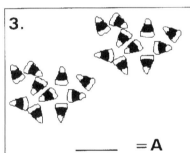
_____ = A

4.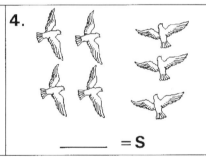
_____ = S

5.
_____ = T

6.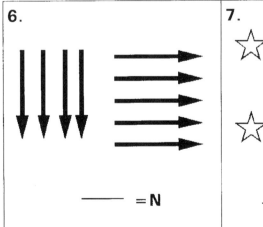
_____ = N

7.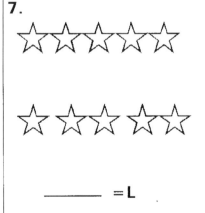
_____ = L

___ ___ ___   ___ ___ ___ ___ ___ ___ ___ ___ ___
6   9   20   5   6   20   3   7   5   6   6   10

5

Developing a sense of numbers

NAME _____

CLOWNING AROUND

DIRECTIONS: (1) Write the answers to the problems on the lines under the balloons. (2) Color all balloons orange whose answers are more than 10. (3) Color all balloons yellow whose answers are less than 10.

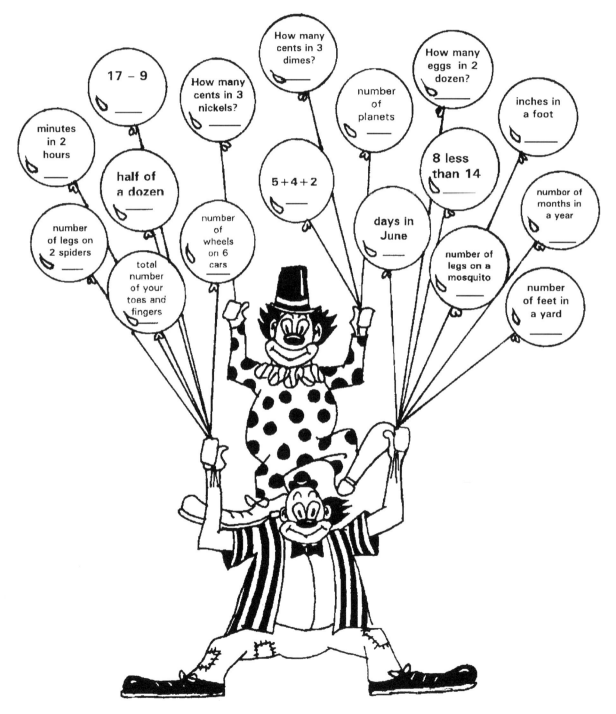

17 – 9
____

How many cents in 3 dimes?
____

How many eggs in 2 dozen?
____

inches in a foot
____

minutes in 2 hours
____

How many cents in 3 nickels?
____

number of planets
____

minutes in 2 hours

half of a dozen
____

5 + 4 + 2
____

8 less than 14
____

number of legs on 2 spiders
____

number of wheels on 6 cars
____

days in June
____

number of months in a year
____

total number of your toes and fingers
____

number of legs on a mosquito
____

number of feet in a yard
____

Practicing with families of facts

NAME _____

Families of Facts

DIRECTIONS: Write the fact family for each triangle. One has been done for you.

Triangle: 12, +, -, 8, 4

1. 8 + 4 = 12
2. 4 + 8 = 12
3. 12 – 8 = 4
4. 12 – 4 = 8

2.

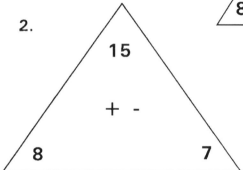

Triangle: 15, + -, 8, 7

1. _____ + _____ = _____
2. _____ + _____ = _____
3. _____ - _____ = _____
4. _____ - _____ = _____

3.

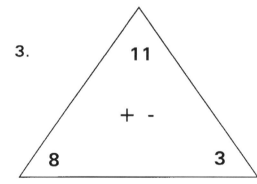

Triangle: 11, + -, 8, 3

1. _____ + _____ = _____
2. _____ + _____ = _____
3. _____ - _____ = _____
4. _____ - _____ = _____

4.

Triangle: 9, + -, 4, 5

1. _____ + _____ = _____
2. _____ + _____ = _____
3. _____ - _____ = _____
4. _____ - _____ = _____

7

Practicing subtraction facts

Up, Up, and Away in My Hot Air Balloon

NAME _____

DIRECTIONS: Solve all problems and write your answers on the lines. Use the code to color the balloons.

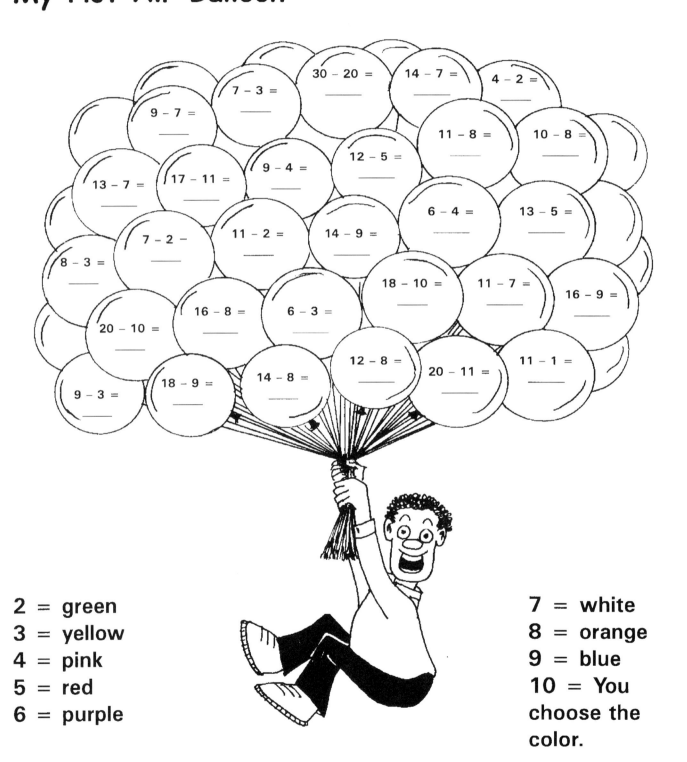

2 = green
3 = yellow
4 = pink
5 = red
6 = purple

7 = white
8 = orange
9 = blue
10 = You choose the color.

Using dominoes for addition and subtraction facts **NAME** ____________________

LET'S TRY IT WITH DOMINOES!

DIRECTIONS: Write 1 addition fact and 1 subtraction fact for each domino. One has been done for you.

1. 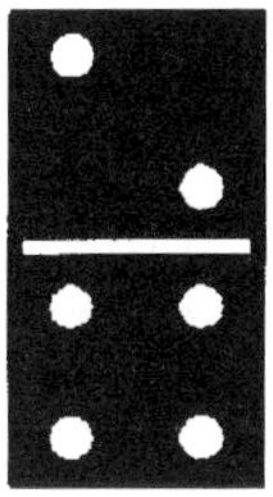

$2 + 4 = 6$ $\quad$ $6 - 2 = 4$

2. 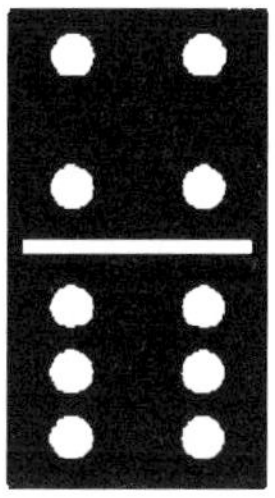

+ ☐ ☐ $\quad$ - ☐ ☐

3. 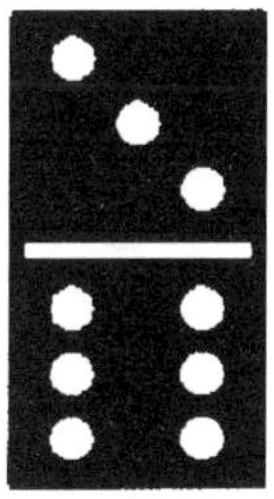

+ ☐ ☐ $\quad$ - ☐ ☐

4. 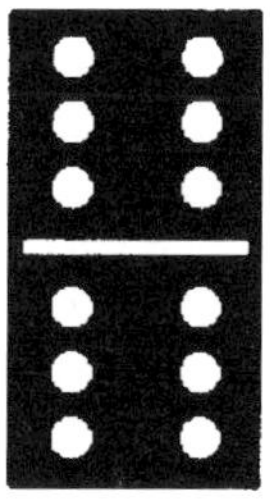

+ ☐ ☐ $\quad$ - ☐ ☐

5. 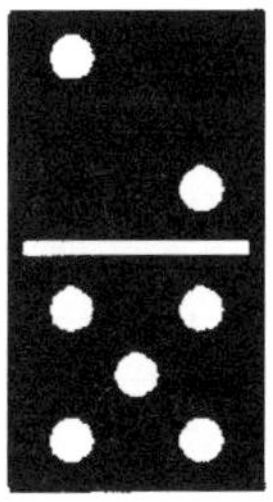

+ ☐ ☐ $\quad$ - ☐ ☐

6. 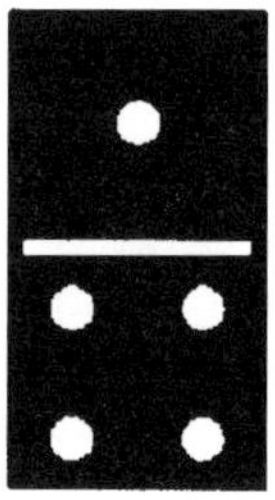

+ ☐ ☐ $\quad$ - ☐ ☐

7. 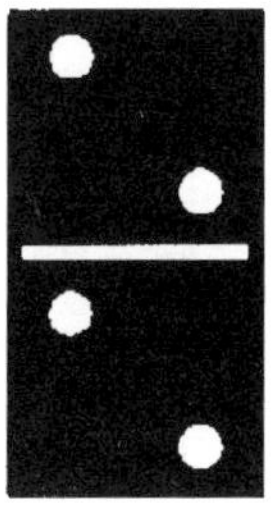

+ ☐ ☐ $\quad$ - ☐ ☐

8. 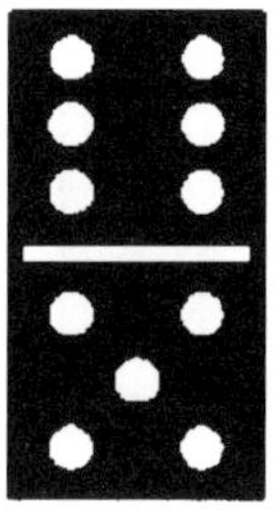

+ ☐ ☐ $\quad$ - ☐ ☐

Adding with facts from 1-20

The Doggie and Bone Show   NAME _____

DIRECTIONS: The doggie wants to get to his bone. First, work all the problems. Then, draw a path through boxes with sums of 8, 11, and 13. You can go across, down, or diagonally.

	1 +4	4 +3	7 +3	5 +9	5 +6	4 +1
9 +4 = 13	7 +4 = 11	8 +9	6 +7	3 +5	4 +0	6 +5
9 +9	6 +7	5 +4	1 +10	3 +6	10 +3	4 +10
5 +3	9 +1	7 +5	6 +2	7 +7	2 +9	7 +1
0 +4	4 +4	10 +4	10 +1	1 +8	10 +0	6 +5
9 +7	2 +9	9 +10	10 +10	6 +10	3 +9	0 +7
8 +0	8 +2	6 +1	9 +0	4 +9	6 +6	9 +8
7 +7	7 +4	1 +3	6 +2	6 +8	3 +5	4 +8
6 +6	6 +8	5 +8	4 +2	2 +0	9 +6	10 +1
0 +3	5 +10	8 +4	9 +0	1 +10	4 +4	6 +6
4 +6	2 +1	6 +9	5 +9	6 +4	5 +7	

Finding the missing number   NAME _____

Poor Farmer Johnson!

This little bunny and her friends have eaten a lot of Farmer Johnson's new garden. Help Farmer Johnson figure out how much of his garden is left.

Farmer Johnson planted:

6 rows of

5 rows of

10 rows of

6 rows of

8 rows of

12 rows of

The bunnies came to the garden and they ate and ate. They ate:

1 row of

1 row of

2 rows of

3 rows of

2 rows of

5 rows of

DIRECTIONS: Write how many rows Farmer Johnson has left of each of the vegetables shown below:

1. _____ rows of 🍓 are left.   4. _____ rows of 🫛 are left.

2. _____ rows of 🧅 are left.   5. _____ rows of 🫑 are left.

3. _____ rows of 🥕 are left.   6. _____ rows of 🥕 are left.

BONUS: 1. What was the total number of rows planted by Farmer Johnson? _____ (48, 47, or 61)   2. What was the total number of rows left for Farmer Johnson to raise? _____ (31, 33, or 34)

Practicing addition facts

NAME _____

FIND THE WINNING NUMBERS

DIRECTIONS: Draw a line through the numbers that make a winner. You can go across, down, or diagonally. The first one has been done for you.

1. Sum 12

7	8	3
4	3	2
4	3	5

2. Sum 10

6	3	2
4	2	9
4	6	2

3. Sum 14

3	9	4
5	3	4
2	2	4

4. Sum 20

2	8	9
7	11	5
0	2	4

5. Sum 18

2	8	9
7	11	5
0	2	4

6. Sum 24

2	10	4
10	8	6
11	5	9

Brain Ticklers

7. Sum 50

15	20	16
1	31	22
35	2	12

8. Sum 100

22	38	42
58	27	14
19	35	45

Practicing addition facts to 20

NAME _____

Where Is That Ostrich?

DIRECTIONS: Solve the facts. Draw a green square around each fact that has an answer greater than 13.

1. 8 + 6 = _____
2. 9 + 4 = _____
3. 6 + 3 = _____
4. 2 + 2 = _____
5. 3 + 10 = _____
6. 5 + 4 = _____
7. 6 + 6 = _____
8. 2 + 1 = _____
9. 3 + 3 = _____
10. 5 + 5 = _____
11. 2 + 7 = _____
12. 7 + 3 = _____
13. 5 + 6 = _____
14. 4 + 6 = _____
15. 5 + 7 = _____
16. 8 + 4 = _____
17. 9 + 3 = _____
18. 7 + 0 = _____
19. 3 + 8 = _____
20. 7 + 8 = _____

21. 4 + 3 = _____
22. 9 + 1 = _____
23. 2 + 3 = _____
24. 8 + 8 = _____
25. 5 + 3 = _____
26. 1 + 1 = _____
27. 9 + 9 = _____
28. 10 + 2 = _____
29. 6 + 2 = _____
30. 1 + 6 = _____
31. 8 + 3 = _____
32. 9 + 0 = _____
33. 7 + 5 = _____
34. 8 + 9 = _____
35. 6 + 9 = _____
36. 10 + 3 = _____
37. 4 + 0 = _____
38. 9 + 2 = _____
39. 0 + 0 = _____
40. 10 + 9 = _____

41. 2 + 4 = _____
42. 7 + 1 = _____
43. 7 + 6 = _____
44. 8 + 7 = _____
45. 1 + 4 = _____
46. 6 + 9 = _____
47. 7 + 9 = _____
48. 5 + 8 = _____
49. 5 + 1 = _____
50. 4 + 9 = _____

BONUS: If you have **10 green squares**, draw a head on the ostrich. If you haven't drawn ten green squares, recheck your work and then draw a head for the ostrich.

Tic-Tac-Toe

Playing Tic-Tac-Toe to practice addition facts

NAME _____

Players : Two **Materials:** (1) A pair of dice, (2) pencil, and (3) Tic-Tac-Toe handouts

DIRECTIONS: Each player rolls the dice; the player with the highest roll gets to start the game and uses an X. The other player uses an O. The first player rolls the dice and adds the 2 numbers on the dice. If that number is on the game board, the player puts an X over the number. If the number is not on the board, Player One loses his/her turn. The dice is then rolled by the next player. The game continues until one player gets Tic-Tac-Toe. The winning player earns a point. If the game is a draw, both players earn a point.

Let's Play Tic-Tac-Toe!

Game #1

4	5	11
8	3	10
9	6	7

Game #2

6	7	9
10	11	5
8	3	9

Game #3

5	6	11
8	10	4
3	9	7

Game #4

8	5	11
9	7	4
8	6	10

Game #5

5	6	8
11	10	4
9	7	10

Player 1's Name _____

Player 1's Scoreboard (Keep a record of your wins here) : _____

Player 2's Name _____

Player 2's Scoreboard (Keep a record of your wins here) : _____

NAME _____

SKIP COUNTING

DIRECTIONS: Complete the charts below by skip counting.

Skip count by 3s.

15	18	21		27		33		
42		48			57			66

Skip count by 5s.

30			45				65		
	85			100					125

Skip count by 4s.

20	24		32		40			52	
60		68		76		84			96

GOOD FOR YOU!

NAME _____

Making It to the Finish Line!

DIRECTIONS: Help Ralph, the racing dog, get to the finish line. Count by twos to complete the chart.

	30	32	34		38		42	
46			52		56		60	64
66			72		76		82	
86		90		94			100	
106		110		114			120	124
	128		132			138		144
	148			154		158	162	
166		170		174		178		182	
186		190			196			204
	208		212		216		220	

CONGRATULATIONS!
YOU MADE IT!!

NAME _____

What five letter word has six left when two letters are taken away?

DIRECTIONS: Complete the pattern. Find the number in the secret code. Write the letter of the problem above it.

1. 3, 5, 7, 9, _____ = R

2. 6, 8, 10, 12, _____ = H

3. 3, 7, 11, 15, _____ = O

4. 10, 15, 20, 25, _____ = E

5. 6, 14, 22, 30, _____ = D

6. 20, 18, 16, 14, _____ = W

7. 400, 300, 200, _____ = I

8. 66, 55, 44, 33, _____ = T

9. 20, 16, 12, 8, _____ = Y

10. 30, 24, 18, 12, _____ = X

11. 0, 9, 18, 27, _____ = S

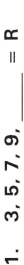

_____ _____ _____ _____
22   14   30

_____
36   100

_____ _____ _____ _____
12   19   11   38

_____ _____ _____
6   22   4

Skip counting by twos

NAME _____

Dot to Dot Mania

DIRECTIONS: Connect by twos.

164
162   166
156   158   170   196 **Start**
154   160 168   172   194   2
152   174   188   192   4
176   186   190   6
184   8
178 180 182   10   38
150   148   12 30   36
146   14   32   40
144   16   28   34 42   44   46
18   26   50   48
20
22
54   24   52
142
140   56
132   134   58
130   106   138   64   66
128   136   60   62   68
104   92
126   102 100 98   94   70
96   90
120   124
122   108   72   76
118   110   88   74
116   114   86   78
112   84   82   80

┌───┐
│ I live part of my life in water and part on land. What am I? _____ │
└───┘

NAME _____

Distinguishing between odd and even numbers

PINWHEELS

DIRECTIONS: Draw a line from each box in the middle of the circle to each **even** number. An example has been done for you.

EXAMPLE

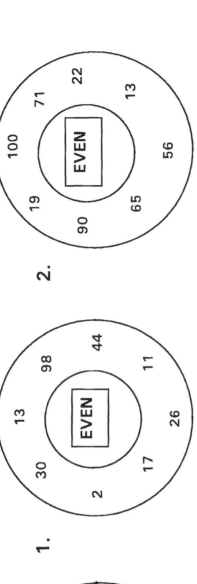

1.

EVEN

30 13 98 44 11 26 17 2

2.

EVEN

100 71 22 13 56 65 90 19

DIRECTIONS: Now, draw a line from each box in the middle of the circle to each **odd** number.

3.

ODD

10 95 44 19 18 15 22 21

4.

ODD

30 13 98 88 11 26 17 2

5.

ODD

1 7 22 11 56 65 90 13

Check yourself!

Did you draw lines to 9 **even** numbers? Yes ____ No ____

Did you draw lines to 12 **odd** numbers? Yes ____ No ____

NAME _____

Name that Number!

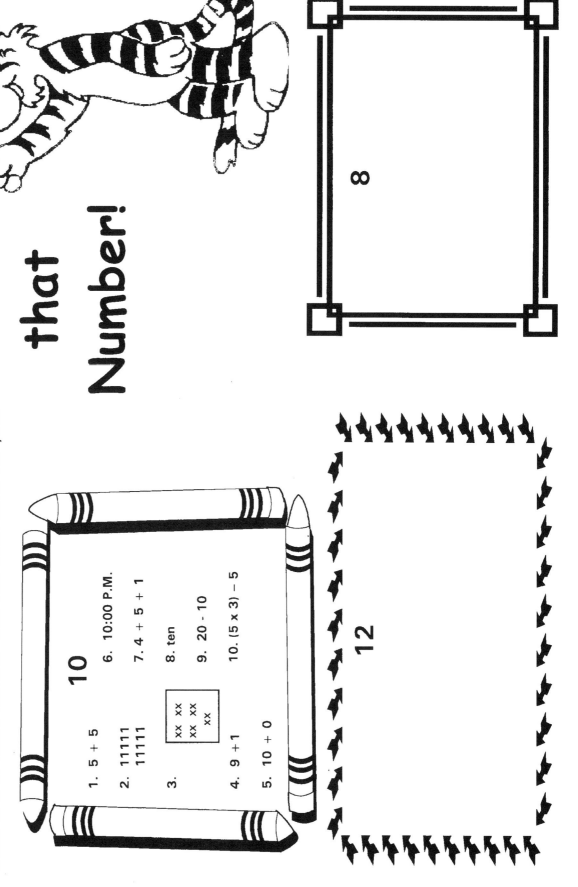

Writing a variety of names for numbers

DIRECTIONS: Think of many, varied, and unusual names for the number shown in each frame. Try to think of **5** or more names. One has been done for you.

10

1. 5 + 5

2. 11111
   11111

3. xx xx
   xx xx
   xx

4. 9 + 1

5. 10 + 0

6. 10:00 P.M.

7. 4 + 5 + 1

8. ten

9. 20 - 10

10. (5 x 3) – 5

8

12

Adding three or more addends

NAME _____

What did the sad and lonely owl say?

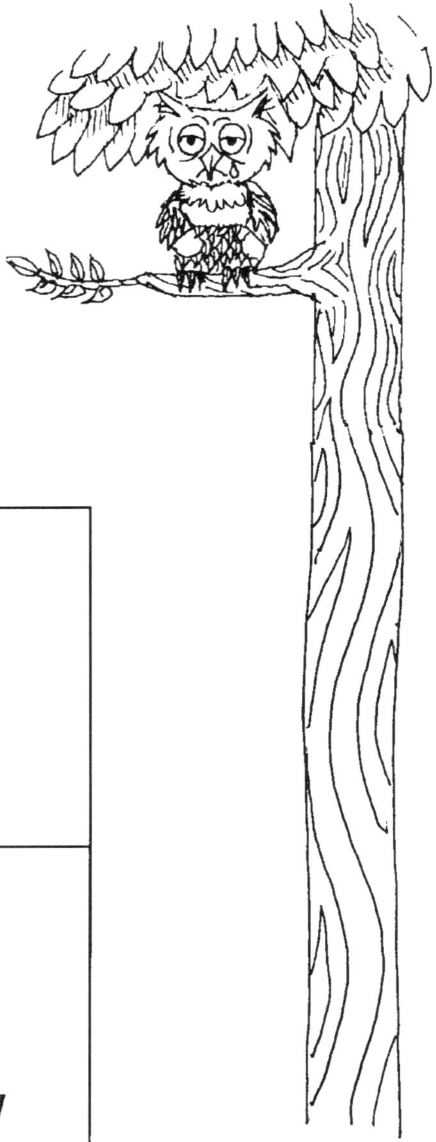

DIRECTIONS: Solve each problem. Find the answer in the secret code. Write the letter of the problem above it.

1. 6 8 +3 = S	2. 3 5 9 +1 = A	3. 5 4 2 1 +2 = E	4. 2 4 5 +4 = O
5. 6 4 +3 = R	6. 9 8 1 +2 = H	7. 3 4 3 +9 = C	8. 3 3 5 4 +6 = W

21 20 15   21 20 15   19 18 13 14 17 ?

Practicing addition with magic squares   NAME _____

MAGIC SQUARES

DIRECTIONS: Find the sum for each magic square. Add down or across but not diagonally. One has been done for you.

1. The **sum** in each row and column is **18**.

3	5	10
6	6	4
9	7	2

2. The **sum** in each row and column is **12**.

	4	6
7		5

3. The **sum** in each row and column is **15**.

	5	1
2		8

4. The **sum** in each row and column is **14**.

7	4	
3		9

5. The **sum** in each row and column is **13**.

	5	
3	4	
8		

6. **Make your own Magic Square and ask a friend to solve it!**

Finding distances between numbers

NAME _____

What gets wetter and wetter the more it dries?

DIRECTIONS: Solve the problems. Find the answer in the secret code. Write the letter of the problem above it. One has been done for you.

1.
46 47 48 49 50 51 52 53 54 55 56 57 58
Hop from 49 to 54. How many jumps? _____ = **O**

2.
81 82 83 84 85 86 87 88 89 90 91 92 93 94
Hop from 84 to 93. How many jumps? _____ = **A**

3.
30 31 32 33 34 35 36 37 38 39 40 41
Hop from 33 to 41. How many jumps? _____ = **E**

4.
45 46 47 48 49 50 51 52 53 54 55 56
Hop from 46 to 52. How many jumps? _____ = **L**

5.
81 82 83 84 85 86 87 88 89 90 91 92
Hop from 81 to 92. How many jumps? _____ = **W**

6.
101 102 103 104 105 106 107 108 109 110
Hop from 103 to 107. How many jumps? _____ = **T**

```
        O
___   ___  ___  ___   ___  ___
 9     4    5    11    8    6
```

23

NAME _____

Using Number Grids

DIRECTIONS: Using the grid below, find the distances between the numbers given at the bottom of the page. Circle your answers, which you can find listed at the bottom of the page. The first one has been done for you.

1	2	3	4	5	6	7	8	9	10
11	12	13	14	15	16	17	18	19	20
21	22	23	24	25	26	27	28	29	30
31	32	33	34	35	36	37	38	39	40
41	42	43	44	45	46	47	48	49	50
51	52	53	54	55	56	57	58	59	60
61	62	63	64	65	66	67	68	69	70
71	72	73	74	75	76	77	78	79	80
81	82	83	84	85	86	87	88	89	90
91	92	93	94	95	96	97	98	99	100
101	102	103	104	105	106	107	108	109	110
111	112	113	114	115	116	117	118	119	120

1. 101 and 113 ___11___
2. 65 and 69 _____
3. 76 and 87 _____
4. 12 and 2 _____
5. 116 and 118 _____

6. 27 and 42 _____
7. 98 and 82 _____
8. 30 and 1 _____
9. 74 and 118 _____
10. 20 and 6 _____

14	11	3	9	43	13	28	10	1	15	20

Brain Tickler - What is the greatest distance that can be found on this grid? Circle your answer: **120, 119, 118**

Using the calculator for counting   NAME _____

Calculator "Thinks"

DIRECTIONS: To count by any number, follow the directions given in the box:

Press [the number] and [+]. Then press [=] over and over.

1. Count by 2 on your calculator. Write the missing numbers.

    2 4 ___ ___ ___ ___ 18 ___ ___ ___ ___ 28

2. Count by 3 on your calculator. Write the missing numbers.

    3 6 ___ ___ ___ 21 ___ ___ ___ 33 ___ ___ ___

3. Count by 5 on your calculator. Write the missing numbers.

    5 ___ ___ ___ ___ ___ 35 ___ ___ ___ 55 ___ ___ ___

4. Count by 11 on your calculator. Write the missing numbers.

    11 ___ ___ ___ ___ 66 ___ ___ ___ 110 ___ ___ 143

5. Kyle counted on his calculator. He wrote these numbers: 4, 10, 16, 22, 28.
    What key did he press? _____

6. Anna was counting on her calculator by 9. Circle the number where Anna must
    have made a mistake and hit the wrong key: 9, 18, 27, 35, 44.

7. Count by 7 on your calculator. Write the missing numbers.

    21 28 ___ ___ ___ ___ ___ 70 ___ ___ ___

BRAIN TICKLER: If you were counting by 100, how many times would you press
the [=] key to reach 2000? Circle your answer: **19   20   21**

25

NAME _____

Going on a Number Hunt!

DIRECTIONS: Use the grid to fill in the blanks. Choose from this group of symbols: (◇,#, ⊗,□,☺). One has been done for you.

1. 331 __#__	5. 315 _____	9. 357 _____	13. 397 _____
2. 372 _____	6. 310 _____	10. 350 _____	14. 375 _____
3. 339 _____	7. 303 _____	11. 389 _____	15. 336 _____
4. 344 _____	8. 400 _____	12. 379 _____	16. 386 _____

301		☺		305			◇	309	⊗
	312			⊗	316		⊗		◇
321		□		☺		327	☺		
#	332				#			□	
		343	☺			□	348		☺
☺		#		355		⊗		△	360
361			△			#	368		
	△	373		☺	376	□		#	◇
△			384		⊗		388	◇	
391	◇		#	395	#	△			□

Comparing whole numbers   **NAME** _____

Is it < or > ?

Directions: Decide which number the dragon would eat. Draw the dragon's mouth (< or >) in the circle. Look at the example. **Remember: the dragon's mouth eats the larger number.**

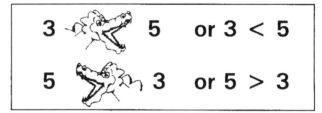

3   5   or 3 < 5

5   3   or 5 > 3

1. 6 ◯ 9

2. 12 ◯ 10

3. 34 ◯ 67

4. 56 ◯ 32

5. 78 ◯ 67

6. 34 ◯ 98

7. 4 ◯ 40

8. 11 ◯ 9

9. 45 ◯ 46

10. 21 ◯ 2

11. 135 ◯ 145

12. 163 ◯ 205

13. 360 ◯ 270

14. 87 ◯ 123

15. 125 ◯ 25

16. 299 ◯ 345

17. 84 ◯ 3

18. 109 ◯ 230

19. 403 ◯ 430

20. 101 ◯ 100

If you have 11 < symbols and 9 > symbols, then draw 3 more flowers for the dragon to smell. If you don't, recheck your work and then draw 3 more flowers for the dragon to smell.

Determining order in whole numbers   NAME _____

What kind of large truck is used to carry a load of pigs?

DIRECTIONS: Solve each problem below. Find your answer in the secret code. Write the letter of the problem above it.

1.   Name the number that comes 1 before 78 = _____   **H**

2.   Name the number that is 5 less than 50 = _____   **N**

3.   Name the number that comes 1 before 100 = _____   **L**

4.   Name the number that is 10 greater than 12 = _____   **I**

5.   Name the number that is 20 less than 30 = _____   **U**

6.   Name the number 12 more than 8 = _____   **T**

7.   Name the number that is between 15 and 17 = _____   **A**

8.   Name the number that comes 1 before 50 = _____   **Q**

9.   Name the number 100 greater than 200 = _____   **E**

10.   Name the number that is between 36 and 38 = _____   **S**

11.   Name the number that comes 1 after 99 = _____   **R**

12.   Name the number that comes between 49 and 51 = _____   **G**

___ ___   ___   ___   ___   ___   ___   ___   ___   ___
16   45   300   22   50   77   20   300   300   45

___   ___   ___   ___   ___   ___   ___   ___
37   49   10   300   16   99   300   100

Determining order in whole numbers   NAME _____

Why did the corn go to the doctor?

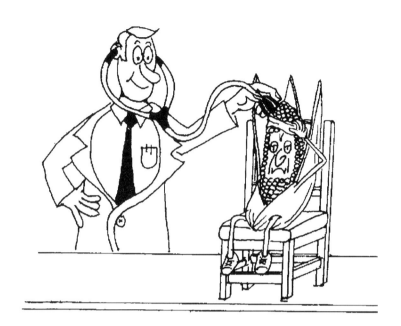

DIRECTIONS: Solve each problem. Find the answer in the secret code. Write the letter of the problem above it.

1.   Name the number that comes one after 33 = _____ **A**

2.   Name the number that is 2 greater than 45 = _____ **N**

3.   Name the number that is 5 less than 21 = _____ **H**

4.   Name the number that is 5 more than 36 = _____ **E**

5.   Name the number that comes between 45 and 47 = _____ **I**

6.   Name the number that is 10 greater than 76 = _____ **T**

7.   Name the number that is 4 less than 19 = _____ **R**

8.   Name the number that is between 88 and 90 = _____ **C**

9.   Name the number that is 8 less than 28 = _____ **D**

_____ _____   _____ _____ _____
  46   86   16   34   20

_____ _____   _____ _____ _____ _____ _____ _____ _____
 34   47   41   34   15   34   89   16   41

Adding with no regrouping   NAME _____

If a ghost made a mistake, what would you call it?

DIRECTIONS: Solve each problem.
Find the answer in the secret code.
Write the letter of the problem above it.

1. 64
  + 35
       = T

2. 37
  + 12
       = A

3. 64
  + 25
       = U

4. 52
  + 13
       = D

5. 12
  + 23
       = I

6. 91
  + 7
       = L

7. 36
  + 23
       = E

8. 57
  + 11
       = W

9. 62
  + 26
       = O

10. 72
  + 13
       = B

___ ___   ___ ___ ___ ___ ___
35   99   68   88   89   98   65

___ ___   ___   ___ ___ ___   ___ ___ ___
85   59   49   85   88   88   85   88   88

Adding with regrouping

NAME _____

When farmers want to start a race, what do they say?

DIRECTIONS: Add. Find the answer in the secret code. Write the letter of the problem above it.

1. 26 +45 ___ =D	2. 36 +29 ___ =T	3. 87 +63 ___ =A	4. 24 +19 ___ =Y
5. 14 +37 ___ =E	6. 89 +37 ___ =R	7. 65 +47 ___ =O	8. 76 +43 ___ =S
			9. 35 +93 ___ =H

___ ___ ___ ___ ___ , ___ ___ ___ ___ ___ , ___ ___ ___ !
126 51 150 71 43   71 51 119 51 65   128 112 51

©2004 by Incentive Publications, Inc., Nashville, TN.

Adding with no regrouping and regrouping

NAME _____

What does a sidewalk become in an ice storm?

DIRECTIONS: Add. Find your answer in the secret code. Write the letter of the problem above it.

| 1. $\begin{array}{r} 341 \\ 23 \\ +104 \\ \hline \end{array}$ = D | 2. $\begin{array}{r} 345 \\ 205 \\ +64 \\ \hline \end{array}$ = E | 3. $\begin{array}{r} 621 \\ 93 \\ 578 \\ +34 \\ \hline \end{array}$ = W | 4. $\begin{array}{r} 65 \\ 10 \\ 234 \\ +145 \\ \hline \end{array}$ = L |
| 5. $\begin{array}{r} 645 \\ 901 \\ 9 \\ +231 \\ \hline \end{array}$ = I | 6. $\begin{array}{r} 134 \\ 45 \\ +367 \\ \hline \end{array}$ = A | 7. $\begin{array}{r} 342 \\ 503 \\ +16 \\ \hline \end{array}$ = K | 8. $\begin{array}{r} 23 \\ 34 \\ +102 \\ \hline \end{array}$ = S |

$\overline{}$ 546 $\overline{}$ 159 $\overline{}$ 454 $\overline{}$ 1,786 $\overline{}$ 468 $\overline{}$ 614 $\overline{}$ 1,326 $\overline{}$ 546 $\overline{}$ 454 $\overline{}$ 861

NAME _____

Using stack addition

What belongs to you but other people use it more than you do?

DIRECTIONS: Use stack addition to solve these problems. Find your answer in the secret code. Write the letter of the problem above it.

Example:
```
  43
 +59
  12 (3 + 9)
 +90 (40 + 50)
 102
```

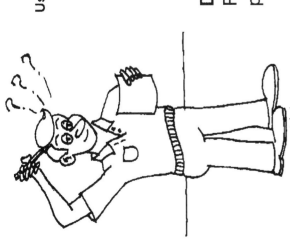

1. 54 +35 = O	2. 64 +39 = A	3. 67 +49 = U
4. 88 +32 = R	5. 47 +89 = M	6. 99 +99 = E
7. 50 +25 = N	8. 46 +27 = Y	

___ ___ ___ ___ ___ ___ ___ ___
73   89   116 120 75   103 136 198

NAME _____

Adding with no regrouping and regrouping

What does a dentist call his x-rays?

DIRECTIONS: Solve each problem. Find your answer in the secret code. Write the letter of the problem above it.

1. 657 +354 = S	2. 431 +167 = A	3. 87 98 +129 = O	4. 982 +340 = N	5. 302 34 +183 = H	6. 356 145 + 48 = I	7. 459 35 +568 = R
8. 333 +777 = T	9. 34 450 63 + 4 = K	10. 805 +134 = C	11. 329 409 + 32 = E	12. 450 450 +450 = W	13. 68 834 +560 = Y	14. 35 4 +156 = P

1,110 519 770 1,462 1,110 1,062 770 314

1,110 519 551 1,322 195 314 549 1,350

1,322 1,350 549 939 1,011

598 1,011

Subtracting without regrouping   NAME _____

Why was the teacher cross-eyed?

DIRECTIONS:
Subtract. Find your answer in the secret code. Write the letter of the problem above it.

1. 55
 -44
   = U
	2. 99
	 -83
	   = R
		3. 67
		 -54
		   = C
			4. 56
			 -21
			   = L
				5. 36
				 -12
				   = H

6. 97
 -30
   = I
	7. 67
	 - 4
	   = S
		8. 56
		 -33
		   = P
			9. 50
			 -10
			   = E
				10. 49
				 -21
				   = O

	11. 89
	 - 2
	   = D
		12. 97
		 - 26
		   = N
			13. 52
			 - 40
			   = T	

___   ___   ___   ___   ___   ___   ___   ___   ___ , ___
63   24   40   13   28   11   35   87   71   12

    ___   ___   ___   ___   ___   ___   ___
    13   28   71   12   16   28   35

___   ___   ___   ___   ___   ___   ___   ___   ___
24   40   16   23   11   23   67   35   63

Subtracting with regrouping

Where is an astronaut's favorite place on a computer?

DIRECTIONS: Subtract. Find your answer in the secret code. Write the letter of the problem above it.

Example:

tens	ones
4	13
5	3
-1	7
3	6

1.

tens	ones
4	3
-2	4
	= E

2.

tens	ones
8	8
-4	9
	= A

3.

tens	ones
7	4
- 4	6
	= T

4.

tens	ones
9	2
- 3	8
	= R

5.

tens	ones
2	3
-1	4
	= C

6.

tens	ones
8	7
-5	8
	= H

7.

tens	ones
5	1
-3	8
	= P

8.

tens	ones
8	0
-6	2
	= S

9.

tens	ones
9	8
-4	9
	= B

28	29	19	18	13	39	9	19	49	39	54

Finding the missing addend   NAME _____

What does a train say when it sneezes?

DIRECTIONS: Solve each problem. Find the answer in the secret code. Write the letter of the problem above it.

1.	_____ + 22 = 32 (I)
2.	16 + _____ = 24 (E)
3.	20 + _____ = 42 (S)
4.	_____ + 15 = 30 (A)
5.	14 + _____ = 28 (C)
6.	_____ + 25 = 50 (H)
7.	30 + _____ = 62 (T)
8.	_____ + 22 = 55 (G)
9.	18 + _____ = 38 (O)

___ ___   ___ ___ ___ ___   ___ ___ ___ -
10   32   33 20 8   22   15 25 25

___ ___ ___ ___   ___ ___ ___ ___
14 25 20 20   14 25 20 20

Subtracting using sequential steps   NAME_____

What do you call a boy named Lee who wants to be by himself all the time?

DIRECTIONS: Solve each problem. Find the answer in the secret code. Write the letter of the problem above it.

| | *Subtract ones* | *Subtract tens* | *Subtract hundreds* |

EXAMPLE

Subtract ones

		3	12
	8	4	2
−	4	9	3
			9

Subtract tens

	7	13	12
	8	4	2
−	4	9	3
		4	9

Subtract hundreds

	7	13	12
	8	4	2
−	4	9	3
	3	4	9

	6	4	5
−	2	5	7

1. _____ = (N)

	8	3	1
−	2	6	2

2. _____ = (O)

	9	9	8
−	2	5	9

3. _____ = (Y)

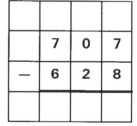

	7	0	7
−	6	2	8

4. _____ = (E)

	7	9	2
−	4	9	3

5. _____ = (L)

____ ____ ____ ____ ____ ____
299 569 388 79 299 739

Subtracting with no regrouping and regrouping

NAME _____

What time is spelled forward and backward yet remains the same?

DIRECTIONS: Subtract. Find the answer in the secret code. Write the letter of the problem above it.

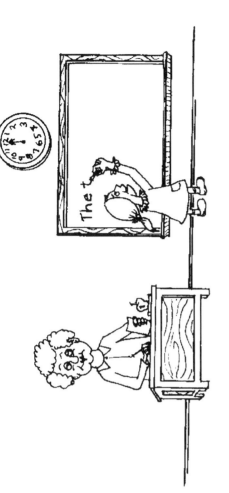

1. 31
   -12
   ___ = H

2. 86
   -41
   ___ = S

3. 62
   -19
   ___ = R

4. 98
   -56
   ___ = I

5. 37
   -14
   ___ = E

6. 74
   -71
   ___ = D

7. 84
   -71
   ___ = T

8. 61
   -12
   ___ = W

9. 55
   -23
   ___ = O

10. 86
   -14
   ___ = N

"____ ____ ____ ____ ____"
  42   13   42   45   3

"____ ____ ____ ____ ____ ____ ____ ____"
  49   32   43   13   72   32   19   23

____ ____
 32   72

Skip counting by threes

NAME _____

DOT TO DOT SUPER CHALLENGE!

DIRECTIONS: Connect by threes.

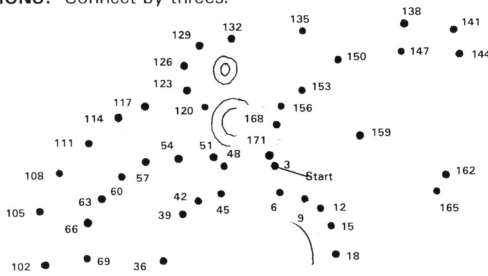

135
138
141
129 132
150 147 144
126
123 153
117 120 156
114 168 159
111 54 51 156
48 171
108 57 3
Start
60 42 162
63 45 6 12 165
105 39 9 15
66 18

102 69 36

72

99

75

78

81
96

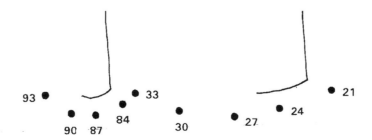

93 33
21
90 87 84 24
30 27

★★★
★
★ I help save lives. I am a _ ir _ ex __ i __ gui __ __ e __. ★
★   ★
★★★

Adding and subtracting with regrouping

NAME _____

Why did the turkey get to join the rock band?

DIRECTIONS: Solve each problem and then find your answer in the secret code. When you find the answer, write the letter of the problem above it.

| 1. $\begin{array}{r} 47 \\ +38 \\ \hline \end{array}$ = U | 2. $\begin{array}{r} 65 \\ -36 \\ \hline \end{array}$ = S | 3. $\begin{array}{r} 89 \\ +73 \\ \hline \end{array}$ = I | 4. $\begin{array}{r} 45 \\ +19 \\ \hline \end{array}$ = K | 5. $\begin{array}{r} 88 \\ -49 \\ \hline \end{array}$ = T | 6. $\begin{array}{r} 51 \\ -39 \\ \hline \end{array}$ = C |
| 7. $\begin{array}{r} 88 \\ +65 \\ \hline \end{array}$ = H | 8. $\begin{array}{r} 23 \\ -19 \\ \hline \end{array}$ = M | 9. $\begin{array}{r} 75 \\ +34 \\ \hline \end{array}$ = R | 10. $\begin{array}{r} 47 \\ +45 \\ \hline \end{array}$ = A | 11. $\begin{array}{r} 47 \\ -28 \\ \hline \end{array}$ = D | 12. $\begin{array}{r} 35 \\ +19 \\ \hline \end{array}$ = E |

$\overline{19}$ $\overline{153}$ $\overline{109}$ $\overline{54}$ $\overline{85}$ $\overline{153}$ $\overline{4}$ $\overline{29}$ $\overline{92}$ $\overline{39}$ $\overline{19}$ $\overline{162}$ $\overline{39}$ $\overline{12}$ $\overline{153}$ $\overline{64}$ $\overline{54}$ $\overline{29}$

40

41

I Spy!

DIRECTIONS: Sammy, the spy, needs your help in checking his work. If Sammy's answer is correct, draw a ☺ next to it. If his answer is incorrect, draw a ☹ next to it.

1. 84
   - 65
    19 ☺
	2. 840
	   + 621
	  1,361
		3. 379
		    682
		  + 901
		  1,963

4. 3,981
   - 1,496
   2,485
	5. 836
	    94
	  + 13
	  933
		6. 400
		   - 98
		  302

7. 906
  -243
  663
	8. 92
	  - 38
	  54
		9. 16
		   49
		 + 37
		 112

Do you have **5** happy faces and **4** sad faces?
Yes ___ No ___ If not, check your work. Sammy wants to thank you for your help.

NAME _____

Patterning with whole numbers

LEAP FROG

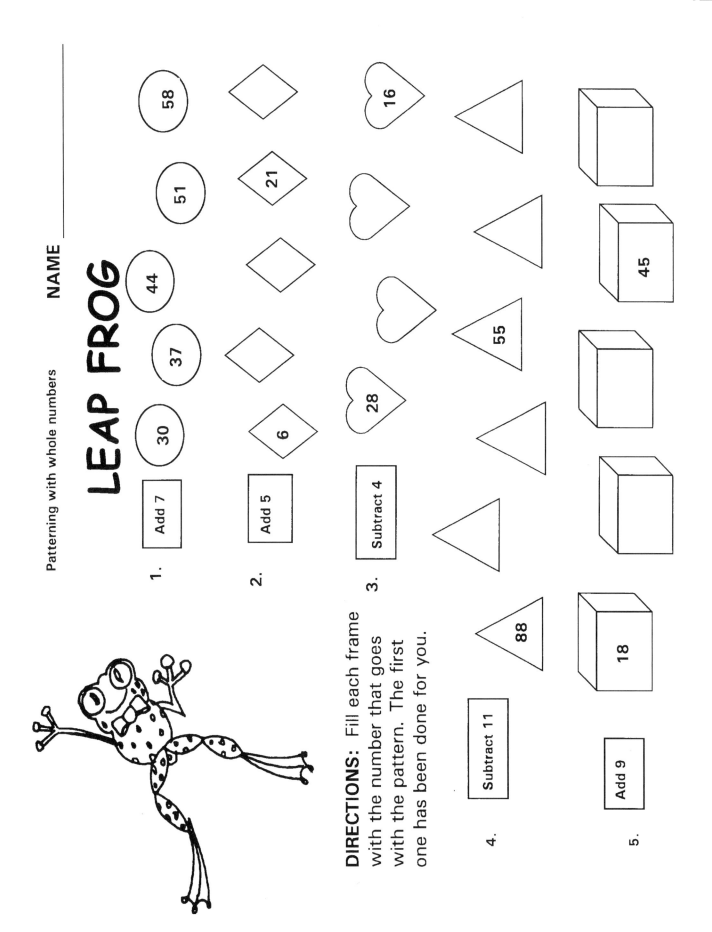

1. | Add 7 | 30 | 37 | 44 | 51 | 58 |

2. | Add 5 | 6 | 21 |

3. | Subtract 4 | 28 | 55 | 16 |

DIRECTIONS: Fill each frame with the number that goes with the pattern. The first one has been done for you.

4. | Subtract 11 | 88 |

5. | Add 9 | 18 | 45 |

Using creative thinking

Let's think together!

NAME _____

We Go Together!

DIRECTIONS: Think of many, varied, and unusual things that go together in a special way.

Make a list of things that come in **twos:** (Try to think of at least **5**).

1. your ears _____
2. _____
3. _____
4. _____
5. _____
6. _____
7. _____
8. _____

Make a list of things that come in **tens:**
1. all of your fingers _____
2. _____
3. _____
4. _____

Make a list of things that come in **sevens:**
1. the days of the week _____
2. _____
3. _____
4. _____

Make a list of things that come in **fives:**
1. the vowels: a,e,i,o,u _____
2. _____
3. _____
4. _____

Make a list of things that come in **fours:**
1. four leaf clover _____
2. _____
3. _____
4. _____

Super Brain Tickler: Think of many, varied, and unusual things that come in **100s.**

Try to think of at least **2:** _____ , _____

Writing standard numerals

What do ghosts wear when it rains?

DIRECTIONS: Write the numeral for each word name given below. Find your answer in the secret code. Write the letter of the problem above it.

1. thirty-six = _____ Y

2. seventy-three = _____ A

3. twenty-three = _____ S

4. forty-seven = _____ W

5. two hundred two = _____ E

6. eight hundred forty-five = _____ R

7. nine hundred four = _____ T

8. five hundred twenty-six = _____ O

9. four hundred twelve = _____ H

10. six hundred seventy-two = _____ B

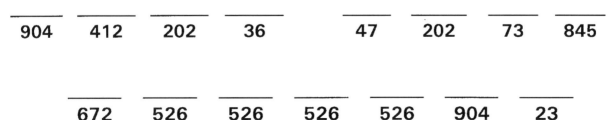

| 904 | 412 | 202 | 36 | | 47 | 202 | 73 | 845 |

| | 672 | 526 | 526 | 526 | 526 | 904 | 23 |

45

NAME _____

What did the big chimney say to the small chimney?

DIRECTIONS: Write the numerals for the word names given below. Find your answer in the secret code. Write the letter of the problem above it.

1. three hundred ten = _____ **A**

2. three thousand, two hundred, six = _____ **T**

3. forty-six = _____ **O**

4. seven hundred thirty-three = _____ **G**

5. seven thousand, three hundred three = _____ **U**

6. four hundred forty-five = _____ **M**

7. thirty-five = _____ **Y**

8. three thousand, six = _____ **R**

9. two hundred forty-six = _____ **N**

10. two thousand, four hundred, two = _____ **K**

11. three hundred thirty-five = _____ **S**

12. four hundred twenty-two = _____ **E**

| 35 | 46 | 7,303 | | 310 | 3,006 | 422 | | 3,206 | 46 | 46 |

| 35 | 46 | 7,303 | 246 | 733 | | 3,206 | 46 | | 335 | 445 | 46 | 2,402 | 422 |

Practicing with place value

NAME _____

What's in a picture?

DIRECTIONS: Use the information in the picture frame to create a number. Write your answer in the space under each frame. Circle your answer at the bottom of the page.

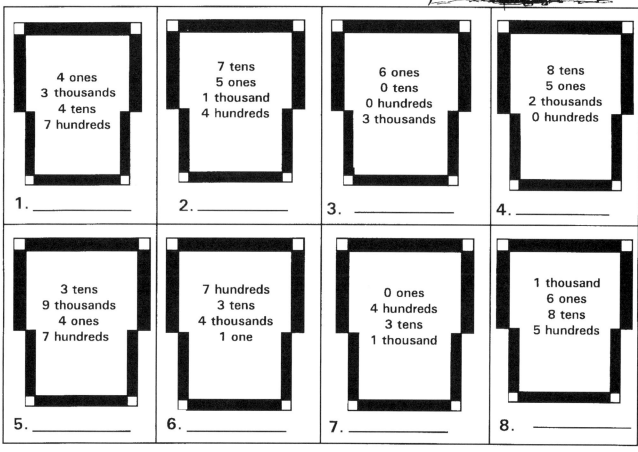

1.

4 ones
3 thousands
4 tens
7 hundreds

2.

7 tens
5 ones
1 thousand
4 hundreds

3.

6 ones
0 tens
0 hundreds
3 thousands

4.

8 tens
5 ones
2 thousands
0 hundreds

5.

3 tens
9 thousands
4 ones
7 hundreds

6.

7 hundreds
3 tens
4 thousands
1 one

7.

0 ones
4 hundreds
3 tens
1 thousand

8.

1 thousand
6 ones
8 tens
5 hundreds

3,006	3,744
1,430	4,731
1,586	2,085
1,475	9,734

Activities with Hundreds Chart

NAME _____

ACTIVITY 1

Materials- Hundreds Chart, 50 counters

Directions: Pair up your students and give each pair of students a copy of the Hundreds Chart and 50 counters (jellybeans, dried beans, popcorn seeds, etc.) Give the student partners a number between two and ten. Ask students to count (skip count) by that number. For example, if the number 3 were called, the students would put counters on the multiples of 3. Ask students to share their comments about patterns that they created and predict the next number. If time permits, other numbers between 2-10 can be called. Students can clear their charts and perform the process using another number.

ACTIVITY 2

Materials - Hundreds Chart for each students, transparency of Hundreds Chart for teacher, 7 crayons or colored markers - Activity can be used with small groups or the total class.

Directions: Students have their Hundred Charts and markers on their desk. Some suggestions for discovering patterns are: (_Some numbers may be colored with more than one marker._)

(1)   Color all of the odd numbers with a blue marker.
(2)   Color all the numbers where both digits are the same with a green marker. (Example : 11)
(3)   Color all the numbers whose digits add up to 7 with a red marker. (Example: 34: 3 + 4 = 7)
(4)   Color all the number that end in zero with a purple marker.
(5)   Color all numbers where the first digit is smaller than the second with a pink marker. (Example : 29)
(6)   Skip count by 4s starting with 20. Color these numbers with a yellow marker.
(7)   Skip count by 5s starting with 40. Color these numbers with a brown marker.

**Note: The teacher can use the transparency to color along as the students work on the various activities with their Hundreds Chart.   In other following lessons, many other pattern tasks can be completed by the students. Examples are:**
**(1) Skip count by 2, 3, 6, 7, 8, 9, or 10, (2) Color all numbers that have 6 as one of its digits, (3) Color numbers whose digits when added together total 9, and (4) Color all even numbers.**

NAME _____

HUNDREDS CHART

1	2	3	4	5	6	7	8	9	10
11	12	13	14	15	16	17	18	19	20
21	22	23	24	25	26	27	28	29	30
31	32	33	34	35	36	37	38	39	40
41	42	43	44	45	46	47	48	49	50
51	52	53	54	55	56	57	58	59	60
61	62	63	64	65	66	67	68	69	70
71	72	73	74	75	76	77	78	79	80
81	82	83	84	85	86	87	88	89	90
91	92	93	94	95	96	97	98	99	100

49

NAME _____

What is five Q and five Q?

DIRECTIONS: Write each numeral's place value. Find your answer in the secret code. Write the letter of the problem above it. Problem 1 has been done for you.

thousand's period   one's period

649,023

1.	Thousand's place =	9	C
2.	One's place = _____	O	
3.	Ten thousand's place = _____	L	
4.	Hundred's place = _____	E	
5.	Ten's place = _____	N	
6.	Hundred thousand's place = _____	U	

Write each number for the word name. Find the answer in the secret code. Write the letter of the problem above it.

7.	seven hundred thirty-three thousand, three = _____	R
8.	seven thousand, three hundred, three = _____	W
9.	seven hundred, three = _____	M
10.	300,000 + 40,000 + 300 + 4 = _____	Y
11.	3,000 + 400 + 30 + 3 = _____	Q
12.	30,000 + 4,000 + 300 + 3 = _____	T

				•							'		
___	___	___	___		___	___	___	___		___		___	
34,303	0	2	3,433		340,304	3	6	733,003		0			

C

							•	
___	___	___	___	___	___	___		
7,303	0	4	9	3	703	0		

NAME _____

Jumbled Number Facts

DIRECTIONS: Rearrange the numbers in each box to make a multiplication fact. An example has been done for you.

EXAMPLE

5	3
0	6

$5 \times 6 = 30$

1.
6	2
4	4

_____

2.
2	9
8	1

_____

3.
3	6
6	6

_____

4.
6	8
8	4

_____

5.
4	6
4	1

_____

6.
7	9
8	2

_____

7.
3	1
4	2

_____

8.
7	9
4	7

_____

9.
3	7
1	2

_____

10.
9	4
6	5

_____

11.
6	9
7	3

_____

12.
9	1
8	9

_____

World Champion Juggler of Numbers

Completing Magic Squares

NAME _____

Multiplication Magic Squares

DIRECTIONS: Can you discover the "magic" in each of these squares? To the right is an example.

EXAMPLE:

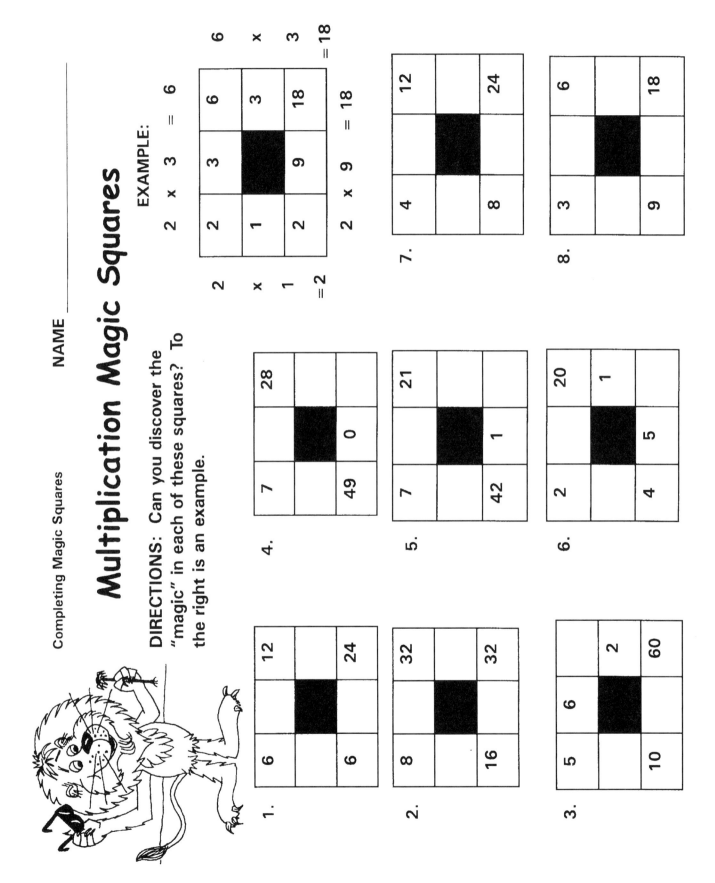

Practicing multiplication facts

NAME _____

Cross Number Puzzle

DIRECTIONS: Solve each problem. Write the answer in the correct boxes going across or down. Use only one digit in each box.

ACROSS

A	3 x 6	B	6 x 5	C	9 x 3
D	6 x 6	E	7 x 5	G	4 x 5
H	10 x 7	I	3 x 7	J	5 x 4
K	7 x 11	L	9 x 4	N	9 x 6
O	5 x 10	P	8 x 7	Q	11 x 4
R	12 x 2	S	6 x 2		

DOWN

A	4 x 4	I	4 x 7	P	5 x 10
E	11 x 3	K	6 x 12	R	2 x 11
F	10 x 7	M	8 x 5	S	9 x 2
H	8 x 9	O	5 x 11	T	5 x 9

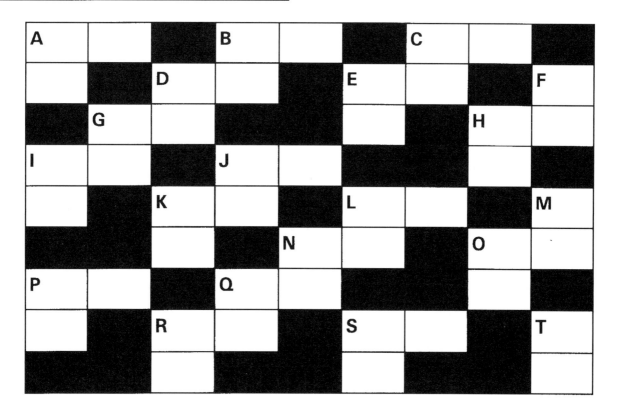

Constructing multiplication arrays

AWESOME ARRAYS

NAME _____

DIRECTIONS: Fill each empty box with an array that you create. Many arrays have been done for you.

×	1	2	3	4	5	6	7	8
X	O	♡ ♡	☆ ☆ ☆	xxxx	*****	KKKKKK	!!!!!!!!	???????
2	x x	xx xx **4**	___	___	***** ***** **10**	___	___	??????? ??????? **16**
3	$ $ $	XX XX XX **6**	: : : **9**	+ + + + + + + + + + + + **12**	___	___	: : : : : : **21**	**24**
4	☺ ☺ ☺ ☺	⇦ ⇦ ⇦ ⇦ ⇦ ⇦ ⇦ ⇦ **8**	___	vvvv vvvv vvvv vvvv **16**	((((((((((((((((((((**20**	___	___	xxxxxxxx xxxxxxxx xxxxxxxx xxxxxxxx **32**

Playing tic-tac-toe to improve multiplication skills   NAME _____

MULTIPLICATION TIC-TAC-TOE

Number of players: 2
Materials: Pair of dice
DIRECTIONS: Each player throws one die and the player with the highest number on the die starts the game. That player then rolls the dice and multiplies the two numbers shown. If the product is on the game board, she marks it with an **X**. If the product is not on the game board, her turn is over. The players alternate taking turns until one player has a Tic-Tac-Toe. A player earns 2 points for each game won. If the game is a draw each player receives 1 point. The overall winner is the player with the most points when all of the rounds have been played.

Round 1

15	24	3
20	12	8
4	10	18

Round 2

12	20	8
15	30	6
5	2	24

Round 3

18	5	10
12	24	6
6	2	15

Round 4

30	6	25
18	12	20
8	3	4

Round 5

15	30	4
12	25	10
5	24	18

Round 6

20	12	24
6	8	30
4	15	2

Players 1's Name _____
Player 1's Score _____

Player 2's Name _____
Player 2's Score _____

Using arrays for multiplication   NAME _____

Multiplication Made Easy With Arrays

DIRECTIONS: For each problem do these three things: (1) make an array, (2) complete the number sentence, and (3) write a word sentence for each array. The first one has been done for you.

1. The music room has 3 rows of chairs with 10 chairs in each row. How many chairs are in the music room?

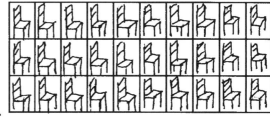

$$3 \times 10 = 30$$

There are <u>30</u> chairs in the music room.

2. For a math lesson, our teacher, Mrs. Dion, gave each person in our small group 8 jellybeans. There were 4 people in our group. How many jellybeans did Mrs. Dion give out?

_____ **x** _____ = _____

Sentence: _____

_____

ARRAY

3. Mom got a sheet of stamps at the post office. Each sheet had 6 rows of stamps and 5 stamps in each row. How many stamps were on the sheet?

_____ **x** _____ = _____

Sentence: _____

_____

ARRAY

4. The small bookstore received 5 boxes of Harry Potter's latest adventure. In each box there were 9 books. How many books were received?

_____ **x** _____ = _____

Sentence: _____

_____

ARRAY

Multiplying single-digit numbers

NAME _____

What do you call someone who walks around with a dictionary?

DIRECTIONS: Solve each problem. Find your answer in the secret code. Write the letter of the problem above it.

Example: (6 x 7) + (3 x 4) =
42 + 12 = 54

1. (3 X 5) + (6 X 3) =

____ + ____ = ____ (R)

2. (7 x 8) + (4 x 5) =

____ + ____ = ____ (M)

3. (1 x 3) + (2 x 4) + (3 x 5) =

____ + ____ + ____ = ____ (Y)

4. (10 x 6) - (5 x 9) =

____ - ____ = ____ (A)

5. (7 x 9) + (6 x 8) =

____ + ____ = ____ (T)

6. (4 x 6) - (9 x 2) =

____ - ____ = ____ (N)

7. (7 x 6) + (8 x 7) + (2 x 5) =

____ + ____ + ____ = ____ (P)

8. (9 x 8) - (5 x 7) =

____ - ____ = ____ (S)

____ ____ ____ ____ ____ ____
37   76   15   33   111   26

____ ____ ____ ____ ____
108   15   6   111   37

©2004 by Incentive Publications, Inc., Nashville, TN.

Solving multiplication story problems

NAME _____

What's the hardest thing about learning to ice skate?

DIRECTIONS: Solve each multiplication story problem and find your answer in the secret code. Each time you find your answer, write the letter of the problem above it. In the empty spaces, you may want to draw a picture, make a diagram, construct an array, or think of your own way to solve the problem.

1. Mom bought 3 boxes of popsicles at the supermarket. Each box had 8 popsicles. How many popsicles were there? _____ = H	
2. Zach has 4 bags of marbles. Each bag has 9 marbles in it. How many marbles does he have? _____ = T	
3. Laura made chocolate chip cookies. She put 5 cookies in each row. There were 6 rows. How many cookies did Laura make? _____ = E	
4. How many wheels are there on 7 bicycles? _____ = C	
5. Mr. DeVigne has 3 boxes of wigs. In each box there are 4 wigs. How many wigs does he have? _____ = I	

36   24   30   12   14   30
___ ___ ___   ___ ___ ___

Multiplying with no regrouping   NAME _____

After you chop down trees, then what do you do with them?

DIRECTIONS: Solve each problem and then find your answer in the secret code. Each time you find your answer in the secret code, write the letter of the problem above it.

1. 34
   x 2
      =T

2. 23
   x 3
      =O

3. 21
   x 7
      =U

4. 33
   x 3
      =E

5. 61
   x 5
      =M

6. 52
   x 4
      =H

7. 71
   x 9
      =P

8. 82
   x 4
      =C

___ ___ ___ ___   ___ ___ ___ ___   ___ ___
328 208 69 639   68 208 99 305   147 639

Multiplying numbers using the stack method

What beans do not grow in a garden?

NAME _____

DIRECTIONS: Solve each problem using stack multiplication. Find your answer in the secret code. Write the letter of the problem above it.

| 1. 82 x 7 = S | 2. 33 x 9 = Y | 3. 25 x 4 = A | 4. 96 x 3 = N |
| 5. 83 x 5 = E | 6. 76 x 6 = B | 7. 98 x 2 = L | 8. 69 x 8 = J |

552 415 196 196 297 456 415 100 288 574

EXAMPLE

6	7
x	3
	21 (7 x3)
+ 1	80 (3 x60)
2	01

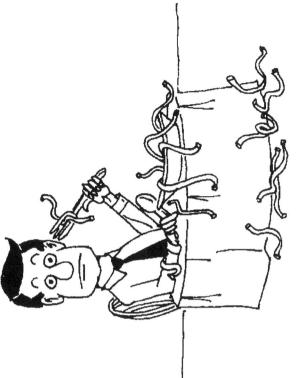

Multiplying with regrouping

NAME _____

Why did the man's spaghetti fall apart?

DIRECTIONS: Solve each problem. Find your answer in the secret code, and write the letter of the problem above it.

1. 63 x 6 =A	2. 35 x 5 =R	3. 16 x 9 = T	4. 74 x 8 = S	5. 93 x 4 =H	6. 72 x 5 =F
7. 43 x 9 =E	8. 14 x 3 =C	9. 39 x 2 =O	10. 56 x 7 =P	11. 25 x 8 =M	12. 56 x 4 =G

___   ___   ___   ___   ___   ___   ___   ___
144 372 387 42 372 387 360 360

___   ___   ___   ___   ___   ___   ___   ___   ___   ___
144 372 387 144 78 200 378 144 78 175 224 78

___   ___   ___   ___   ___
392 592 144 78 387

60

©2004 by Incentive Publications, Inc., Nashville, TN.

Multiplying larger numbers with regrouping

NAME _____

Why are wasps, hornets, and yellow jackets considered above-average insects?

DIRECTIONS: Solve each problem and then find your answer in the secret code. When you find the answer, write the letter of the problem above it.

1. 65 x 5 =R	2. 237 x 8 =H	3. 456 x 9 =A	4. 105 x 3 =N	5. 96 x 6 =Y	6. 76 x 9 =U
7. 438 x 4 =E	8. 381 x 2 =T	9. 56 x 5 =T	10. 33 x 4 =C	11. 897 x 3 =B	12. 364 x 2 =S

2,691 1,752 280 728 684 4,104 1,752 728 1,752 762 1,896 132 1,752 315 728

4,104 325 1,752 2,691 1,752 762 762 684 1,752 576 762 728

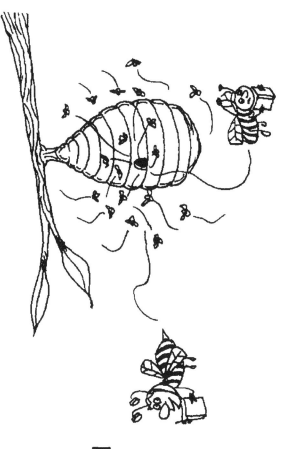

Multiplying two-digit whole numbers   NAME _____

What did the mama broom say to the baby broom?

DIRECTIONS: Solve each problem and then find your answer in the secret code. Write the letter of the problem above it.

1. 65 x 34 = W	2. 87 x 25 = P	3. 21 x 13 = E	4. 89 x 54 = O
5. 87 x 23 = G	6. 99 x 56 = T	7. 45 x 84 = S	

‾‾‾‾‾ ‾‾‾‾‾   ‾‾‾‾‾ ‾‾‾‾‾
2,001   4,806   5,544   4,806

‾‾‾‾‾ ‾‾‾‾‾ ‾‾‾‾ ‾‾‾‾ ‾‾‾‾‾
3,780   2,210   273   273   2,175

Practicing multiplication and division facts

NAME _____

DIRECTIONS: Write the fact family for each triangle. One has been done for you.

Families of Facts!

1.

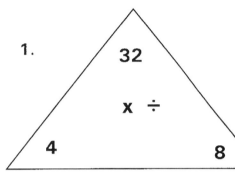

32

x ÷

4   8

1. 4 x 8 = 32
2. 8 x 4 = 32
3. 32 ÷ 4 = 8
4. 32 ÷ 8 = 4

2.

63

x ÷

7   9

1. ___ x ___ = ___
2. ___ x ___ = ___
3. ___ ÷ ___ = ___
4. ___ ÷ ___ = ___

3.

48

x ÷

6   8

1. ___ x ___ = ___
2. ___ x ___ = ___
3. ___ ÷ ___ = ___
4. ___ ÷ ___ = ___

4.

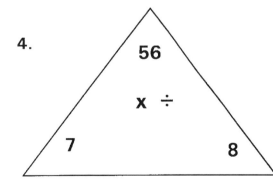

56

x ÷

7   8

1. ___ x ___ = ___
2. ___ x ___ = ___
3. ___ ÷ ___ = ___
4. ___ ÷ ___ = ___

BONUS: On the back write 2-4 triangles of your own and families of facts for each.

Practicing division facts

NAME _____

What does a monster eat after the dentist pulls his tooth?

DIRECTIONS: Solve each problem. Find your answer in the secret code. Write the letter of the problem above it.

> **EXAMPLE:**
> $(20 \div 4) + (36 \div 9) =$
> $\quad 5 \quad + \quad 4 \quad =$

1. $(15 \div 3) + (27 \div 9) = A$
   $\underline{\quad} + \underline{\quad} = \underline{\quad}$
   $\quad A$

2. $(30 \div 5) + (16 \div 4) = I$
   $\underline{\quad} + \underline{\quad} = \underline{\quad}$
   $\quad I$

3. $(27 \div 3) + (27 \div 9) = H$
   $\underline{\quad} + \underline{\quad} = \underline{\quad}$
   $\quad H$

4. $(35 \div 7) + (8 \div 4) = E$
   $\underline{\quad} + \underline{\quad} = \underline{\quad}$
   $\quad E$

5. $(63 \div 9) + (18 \div 3) = D$
   $\underline{\quad} + \underline{\quad} = \underline{\quad}$
   $\quad D$

6. $(20 \div 2) + (81 \div 9) = T$
   $\underline{\quad} + \underline{\quad} = \underline{\quad}$
   $\quad T$

7. $(21 \div 7) + (33 \div 3) = N$
   $\underline{\quad} + \underline{\quad} = \underline{\quad}$
   $\quad N$

8. $(54 \div 6) + (18 \div 9) = S$
   $\underline{\quad} + \underline{\quad} = \underline{\quad}$
   $\quad S$

$$\overline{}\ \overline{} \quad \overline{}\ \overline{}\ \overline{}\ \overline{} \quad \overline{}\ \overline{}\ \overline{} \quad \overline{}\ \overline{}\ \overline{}\ \overline{} \quad \overline{}\ \overline{}\ \overline{}$$
$$12\ 7 \quad 7\ 8\ 19\ 11 \quad 19\ 12\ 7 \quad 13\ 7\ 14\ 19 \quad 10\ 11\ 19$$

Finding quotients   NAME _____

What's the best time of the year to use a trampoline?

DIRECTIONS: Solve each problem and then find your answer in the secret code. When you find the answer, write the letter of the problem above it.

1. 3$\overline{)66}$ = M	2. 8$\overline{)112}$ = N	3. 10$\overline{)120}$ = R
4. 7$\overline{)91}$ = P	5. 2$\overline{)86}$ = E	6. 5$\overline{)85}$ = T
7. 4$\overline{)144}$ = I	8. 9$\overline{)162}$ = G	9. 6$\overline{)150}$ = S

___ ___ ___ ___ ___ ___ ___ ___ ___ ___
25   13   12   36   14   18   17   36   22   43

LOGICAL

THINKING

EXERCISES

and

BRAIN

TICKLERS

Using logical thinking   NAME _____

Case 1-You're the Detective: Which years do kangaroos like the best?

DIRECTIONS: Find the answer to each set of clues. Then find your answer in the secret code and write the letter of the problem above it. You then will have solved the case.

1. I am a number between 10 and 20. I am an even number and I'm greater than 16. What am I? _____ = A

2. I am an odd number that is greater than 30. I am more than 36 and less than 38. What am I? _____ = E

3. I am an odd number. I am less than 40 − 2. I am more than 30 + 3. If you add my digits together you will get 8. What am I? _____ = R

4. I am an odd number that is less than 20. I am more than 2 + 11. If you add my two digits together they will equal 6.
    What am I? _____ = P

5. I am a number that is greater than 9 + 3 and less than 20. I am an odd number. I am between 10 and 15. What am I? _____ = Y

6. I am a number that is less than 20 − 12. I am greater than 5 + 1. What am I? _____ = L

7. I am a number that is more than 20 but less than 30. I am an even number. I am more than 10 + 8 + 9. What am I? _____ = S

___ ___ ___ ___ ___ ___ ___ ___ ___
 7   37   18   15   13   37   18   35   28

Using logical thinking

NAME _____

Case 2 - You're The Detective:
What will not speak unless it is spoken to and cannot be seen but only heard?

DIRECTIONS: Find the answer to each set of clues. Then find your answer in the secret code and write the letter of the problem above it. You will then know the answer to Case 2.

1. I am a number between 50 and 70. I am more than 30 + 35. I am an odd number. I am less than 70 - 1. What am I? _____ = O

2. I am an odd number. I am between 50 and 60. I am less than 30 + 26. Both of my digits are the same. What am I? _____ = H

3. I am an odd number greater than 50 but less than 40 + 25. If you add my two digits together, I will total 9. What am I? _____ = A

4. I am an even number less than 25 but greater than 20. Both of my digits are the same. What am I?
_____ = N

5. I am an even number that is less than 40 - 12. I am more than 3 x 6. I am between 2 x 10 and 2 x 13. If you add my two digits together, they will be more than 5. What am I? _____ = C

6. I am an odd number that is less than 2 x 30. I am more than 70 – 12. What am I? _____ = E

| 63 | 22 | | 59 | 24 | 55 | 67 |

Using logical thinking   NAME _____

Case 3-You're the Detective:
What occurs **once** in every
MINUTE,
twice in every **MOMENT**, but
not once in a
THOUSAND YEARS?

DIRECTIONS: Find the answer to each set of clues. Then find your answer in the secret code and write the letter of the problem above it. You will then have solved the mystery in Case 3.

1. The difference between two numbers is 5. The larger number is 11. What is the smaller number? _____ = H

2. This number is an odd number greater than 4 x 5. It is less than 50 - 25. One of its factors is 7. What is the number? _____ = L

3. The product of two numbers is 48. One factor is 12. What is the other factor? _____ ? = R

4. The sum of two numbers is 19. One number is 1 greater than 13, the other number is less than 10. What is the number? _____ = T

5. This number is an odd number between 21 and 30. It is less than 10 + 15. It is more than 7 x 3. What is the number? _____ = E

6. This number is an odd number between 20 and 30. It is greater than 8 x 3 and less than 10 x 3. One of its factors is 9. What is the number? _____ = M

___   ___   ___   ___   ___   ___   ___   ___   ___   ___
 5   6   23   21   23   5   5   23   4   27

Using logical reasoning

NAME _____

What's in a Shape?

DIRECTIONS: Use the shapes to help you answer each question. Write the answer. The first one has been done for you.

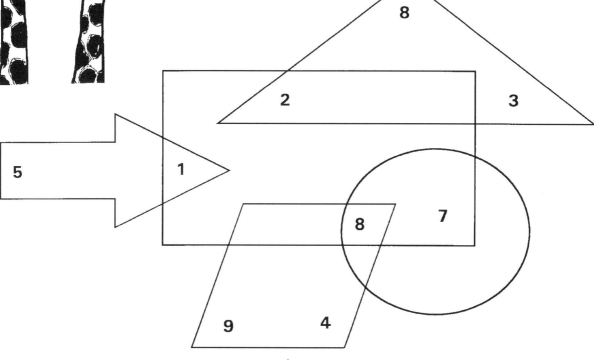

1. What number is in both the △ and the ▭ ? **2**

2. What number is in both the ▱ and the ○ ? _____

3. What is the sum of the numbers in the △ ? _____

4. What is the sum of the numbers in the ▱ ? _____

5. How much more is there in the ▱ than in the △ ? _____

6. Which figure has the lowest sum? (Draw it) _____

7. Which figure has the highest sum? (Draw it) _____

Discovering and using patterns   NAME _____

The Muncher

DIRECTIONS: Use the "In-Out" Rule and fill in the blanks with the missing numbers. Some have been done for you.

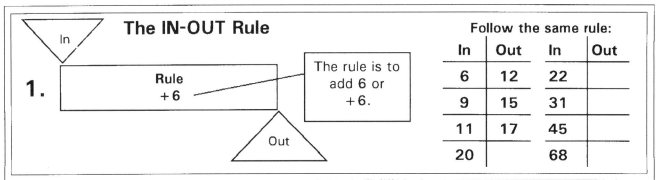

The IN-OUT Rule

1. Rule +6

The rule is to add 6 or +6.

In / Out

Follow the same rule:

In	Out	In	Out
6	12	22	
9	15	31	
11	17	45	
20		68	

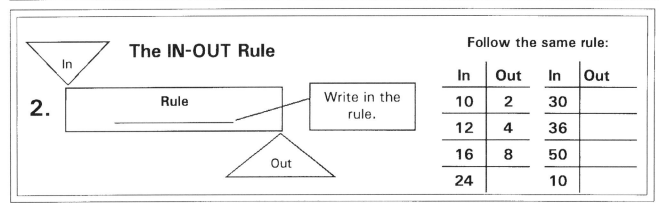

The IN-OUT Rule

2. Rule _____

Write in the rule.

In / Out

Follow the same rule:

In	Out	In	Out
10	2	30	
12	4	36	
16	8	50	
24		10	

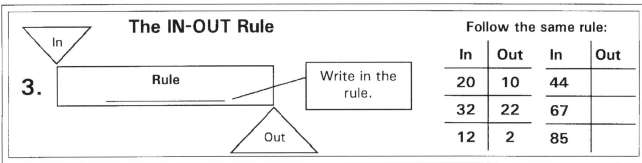

The IN-OUT Rule

3. Rule _____

Write in the rule.

In / Out

Follow the same rule:

In	Out	In	Out
20	10	44	
32	22	67	
12	2	85	

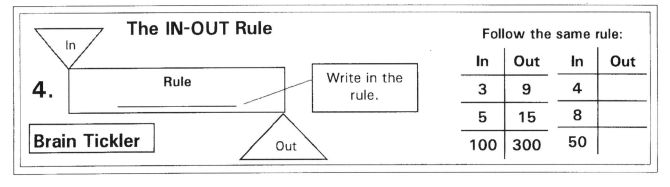

The IN-OUT Rule

4. Rule _____

Write in the rule.

In / Out

Brain Tickler

Follow the same rule:

In	Out	In	Out
3	9	4	
5	15	8	
100	300	50	

Discovering and using patterns   NAME _____

The Muncher No. 2

DIRECTIONS: Use the "In-Out" Rule and fill in the blanks with the missing numbers. Some have been done for you.

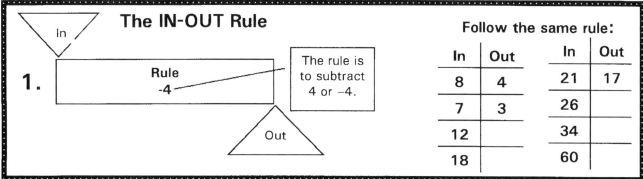

1.

The IN-OUT Rule

In

Rule
-4

The rule is to subtract 4 or −4.

Out

Follow the same rule:

In	Out	In	Out
8	4	21	17
7	3	26	
12		34	
18		60	

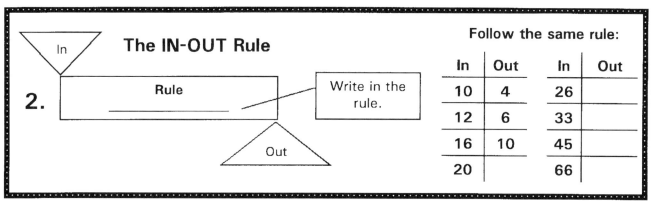

2.

The IN-OUT Rule

In

Rule
_____

Write in the rule.

Out

Follow the same rule:

In	Out	In	Out
10	4	26	
12	6	33	
16	10	45	
20		66	

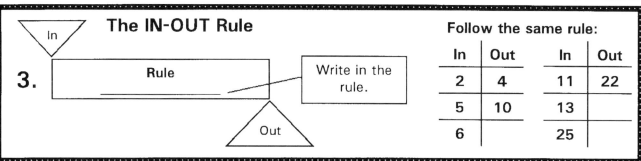

3.

The IN-OUT Rule

In

Rule
_____

Write in the rule.

Out

Follow the same rule:

In	Out	In	Out
2	4	11	22
5	10	13	
6			25

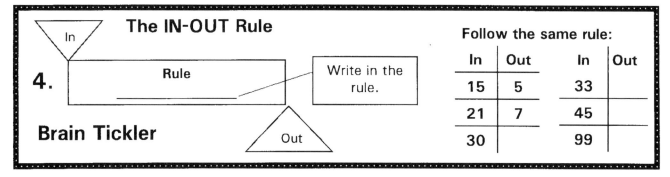

4.

The IN-OUT Rule

In

Rule
_____

Write in the rule.

Out

Brain Tickler

Follow the same rule:

In	Out	In	Out
15	5	33	
21	7	45	
30		99	

Using logic to solve a magic square

NAME _____

MAGIC SQUARE SUPER CHALLENGE

DIRECTIONS: Write 1, 2, 3, and 4 in the boxes so that there is a 1, 2, 3, 4 in each row and column. All columns and rows should total 10.

→ _____ Row 1

→ _____ Row 2

→ _____ Row 3

→ _____ Row 4

↓   ↓   ↓   ↓

CONGRATULATIONS! YOU SOLVED THE PUZZLE!

_____ Column 1   _____ Column 2   _____ Column 3   _____ Column 4

Using logical thinking

NAME _____

It's a Telephone Scavenger Hunt!

DIRECTIONS: Have you noticed that your telephone has letters as well as numbers on it? Match the numbers to the letters on the phone to find the answers to the questions below.

1	ABC 2	DEF 3
GHI 4	JKL 5	MNO 6
PQRS 7	TUV 8	WXYZ 9
*	0	#

1. What insect is in **268**? _____

2. What reptile is in **262**? _____

3. What mammal is in **228**? _____

4. What amphibian is in **3764**? _____

5. What bird is in **32453**? _____

6. Is **728** a rat or a cat? _____

Brain Tickler: Choose from the list below to unlock the names of the foods that can be made from the letters found on your phone:
lettuce fries cookie steak milkshake hot dog tomato ice cream lasagna mushrooms tacos strudel spaghetti candy pizza hamburger

1. 468 364 _____   4. 37437 _____

2. 866286 _____   5. 78325 _____

3. 266543 _____   6. 423 27326 _____

Using logical thinking   NAME _____

The Secret Is in the Arrow

DIRECTIONS: Use **Chart 1: 0-99** to help you solve the problems below. Find your answer in the box at the bottom of the page. Put an **X** in the circle that contains the correct answer.   The first one has been done for you.

1.	23 →→↗↘ = 23→(24) →(25)↗ (16)↘ (27) = <u>27</u>
2.	45 ↗↓→↓← = _____
3.	82 →↙↑→↗ = _____
4.	33→→↑↘→↓ = _____
5.	74←↗↓←↑↗ = _____
6.	55→↑↑→↗→ = _____
7.	4↓↓→↗↗↓ = _____
8.	99←↑↖↖→↓↘ = _____
9.	40→→↘↓→↗ = _____
10.	Create your own arrow pattern and ask a friend to solve it.

©2004 by Incentive Publications, Inc., Nashville, TN.

Using logical thinking   NAME _____

The Secret Is in the Arrow No. 2:
When does Thursday come before Tuesday?

DIRECTIONS: Use **Chart 1: 0-99** to help you solve the problems below. The first one has been done for you. To solve the riddle, find your answer in the secret code at the bottom of the page. Each time your answer appears in the secret code, write the letter of the problem above it.

1.	24 →→↘↘ = 24→(25) →(26)↘ (37 ↘(48) __48__ =		E
2.	40 ↓→↗↓ →↗ =	____ =	A
3.	73↑↑↖←↗→ =	____ =	H
4.	4↓↓↗→→↑ =	____ =	R
5.	55↓→→↙↓ =	____ =	I
6.	39↙↙↑←↑→→ =	____ =	N
7.	9↓↓↓↙↙↓ =	____ =	O
8.	41↗↗←←↑↗ =	____ =	T
10.	93←↑↗↖←↑ =	____ =	C
11.	0↘↘↘↘↘↘ =	____ =	D
12.	20↓→↗↓ →↗ =	____ =	Y

____ ____   ____ ____ ____
86   38   2   33   48

____ ____ ____ ____ ____ ____ ____ ____ ____ ____
66   86   51   2   86   67   38   44   7   24

Chart for "The Secret Is in the Arrow"   **NAME** _____

CHART 1: 0-99

0	1	2	3	4	5	6	7	8	9
10	11	12	13	14	15	16	17	18	19
20	21	22	23	24	25	26	27	28	29
30	31	32	33	34	35	36	37	38	39
40	41	42	43	44	45	46	47	48	49
50	51	52	53	54	55	56	57	58	59
60	61	62	63	64	65	66	67	68	69
70	71	72	73	74	75	76	77	78	79
80	81	82	83	84	85	86	87	88	89
90	91	92	93	94	95	96	97	98	99

Solving word problems   NAME _____

What is the most popular board game ever played?

Clue: It is over 65 years old and the longest game ever played lasted 264 hours.

DIRECTIONS: Solve each problem and then find your answer in the secret code at the bottom of the page. Each time you find your answer, write the letter of the problem above it.

1. How much longer is the world's longest animal, the bootlace worm which measures at 180 feet long, than the blue whale which measures 112 feet long? _____ = **P**

2. Do you know what animal has the most legs? It is the African Millipede which is reported to have 700 legs. The word "millipede" means one thousand legs but no millipede actually has this many legs. How many more legs would the African Millipede need in order to have 1000 legs? _____ = **N**

3. Millions of passenger pigeons once inhabited the banks of Eastern North America; however, due to over-hunting and habitat loss, their numbers greatly decreased in the 19th century. Sadly, the last passenger pigeon died in the Cincinnati Zoo in 1914. In what year will the passenger pigeon have been extinct for 100 years.? _____ = **L**

4. An African elephant can eat up to 770 pounds of food a day. At that rate, how many pounds of food could an African Elephant eat in 2 days? _____ = **Y**

5. Marlins are large fish known for their amazing swimming abilities over long distances. They can swim up to 50 miles an hour. At that speed how far can a Marlin swim in 4 hours? _____ = **O**

6. Are all sharks dangerous to humans? The answer is no. There are 250 species of sharks and only 25 are considered dangerous to humans The most dangerous are the Great White, Hammerhead, Tiger, and Mako. The largest is the Great White and is known for being involved in many attacks on humans. How many species of sharks are not dangerous to human beings? _____ = **M**

225	200	300	200	68	200	2014	1540

79

NAME _____

What did the spider do on the computer?

DIRECTIONS: Solve each problem and then find your answer in the secret code at the bottom of the page. Each time you find your answer, write the letter of the problem above it.

1. The first-ever hot air balloon had **3** special passengers: a rooster, a duck, and a sheep. Their **8**-minute flight took place over Paris, France in **1783**. If the year is **2003**, how many years ago did this balloon flight take place? _____ = **A**

2. Can you believe an anteater can eat up to **30,000** ants in 1 day? It can swoop up as many as **500** ants with a flick of its long, sticky tongue. How many ants can an anteater gobble up with **7** flicks of its tongue? _____ = **D**

3. Do you know that dolls are probably the oldest of toys? They've been made out of rags, wood, wax, china, and plastic. One of the most popular dolls is Barbie. Barbie was first introduced in **1959**. In what year will Barbie be **50** years old? _____ = **I**

4. The first cars weren't allowed to go more than **2** miles per hour. In fact, someone had to walk in front of the car with a flag to warn other people on the road. If you had ridden in one of these cars and wanted to visit your grandmother who lived **50** miles away, how many hours would it have taken you to get to your grandmother's house? _____ = **T**

5. The reticulated python is one of the world's largest snakes. In fact, it can grow as long as a row of six bicycles laid end to end. How many bicycles laid end to end would it take to show the length of **4** pythons? _____ = **E**

6. The largest mammal to have ever lived is the blue whale. It is larger than the largest of the dinosaurs. Blue whales can weigh as much as **150** cars or **150** tons. A ton is equal to **2000** pounds. About how many pounds does the blue whale weigh? _____ = **B**

7. A thirsty camel can drink **10** buckets of water in just **10** minutes. At that rate, how many buckets of water can a camel drink in 1 hour? _____ = **S**

8. An insect has **6** legs. A spider has **8** legs. How many total legs could you count on a bee, mosquito, a tarantula, and a black widow spider? _____ = **M**

9. A queen bee lays so many eggs in a few days that she can only live a couple of years. Imagine! She can lay **3,500** eggs in a day. At that rate, how many eggs could she lay in a week? _____ = **W**

28	220	3,500	24	220	24,500	24	300,000	60	2009	25	24

NAME _____

BRAIN TICKLERS

1.   **How many total squares can you find in the figure below?**
     (Hint: There are many more than 16.)

                    Total of squares you found: _____

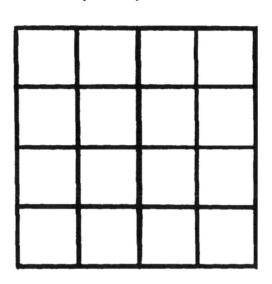

2.   In the Magic Square below, all columns, rows, and diagonals add up to 24.
     AND, it has another special mystery that you will want to discover. To help
     you to make this discovery, you may need to turn your paper and look at the
     square in many different directions.

9	1	8	6
8	6	9	1
6	8	1	9
1	9	6	8

Did you discover the special mystery of this box? _____ Briefly explain.

_____

_____

Using problem solving skills

NAME _____

BRAIN TICKLER NO. 2

1. **DIRECTIONS:** There's a word hidden in the puzzle below. Can you find it?
    (Hint: Try holding the page at several angles.)

    When you find the word, write it here: _____ *Good for you!*

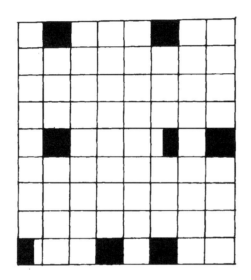 

2. **How many different number combinations on the four circles below total 15? The order of the circles is not important. Two combinations have been done for you. List the other combinations you can make.**

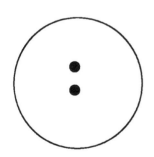 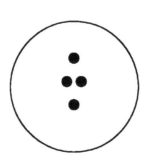 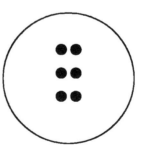 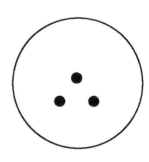

1. 3 + 4 + 6 + 2 = 15	5.	9.
2. 3 + 6 + 2 + 4 = 15	6.	10.
3.	7.	11.
4.	8.	12.

Using problem solving skills   NAME _____

BRAIN TICKLER No. 3

Hit the Target!

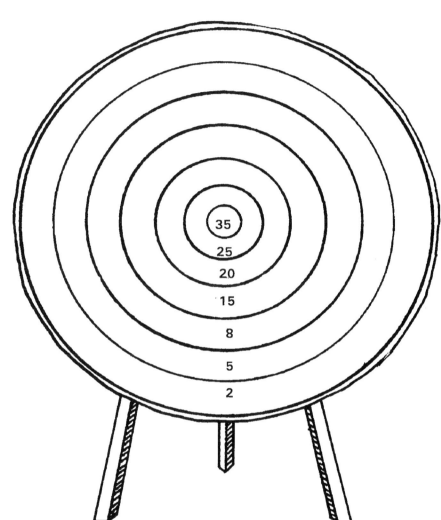

DIRECTIONS: Using the numbers on the dart board, find the numbers when added together will total the numbers below. The first has been done for you.

1. 40 = <u>5</u> + <u>15</u> + <u>20</u>   6. 70 = ___ + ___ + ___ + ___ + ___

2. 33 = ___ + ___ + ___   7. 38 = ___ + ___ + ___

3. 60 = ___ + ___ + ___ + ___   8. 100 = ___ + ___ + ___ + ___ + ___

4. 42 = ___ + ___ + ___   9. 15 = ___ + ___ + ___

5. 65 = ___ + ___ + ___ + ___   10. 45 = ___ + ___ + ___

Using logical thinking

NAME _____

BRAIN TICKLER No. 4: 30s Mania

DIRECTIONS: By adding, subtracting, multiplying or dividing, make the following sets of 4 numbers equal 30! The first one has been done for you.

1.

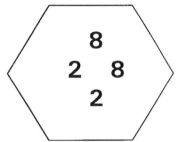

8
2   8
2

8 X 8 = 64 ÷ 2 = 32 − 2 = 30

2.

6
2   3
9

= 30

3.

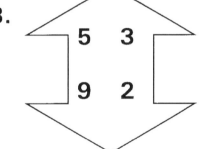

5   3
9   2

= 30

4.

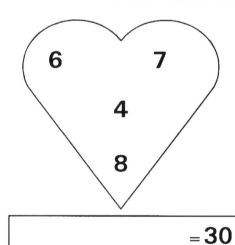

6   7
4
8

= 30

5.

9
3   5   8

= 30

6.

5
6   5   5

= 30

Using logic to solve 2 and 3-step pattern equations

NAME _____

The IN-OUT Super Challenge

DIRECTIONS: Some charts have more than one step. Complete this IN-OUT chart. Use each number in the IN list. Write the answer in the OUT list. The first problem has been done for you on each IN-OUT problems' chart.

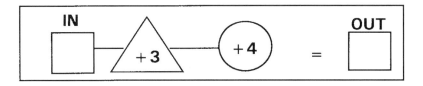

	IN	OUT
1.	6	13
2.	2	
3.	5	
4.	7	

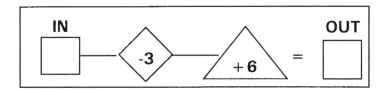

	IN	OUT
5.	5	8
6.	10	
7.	12	
8.	4	

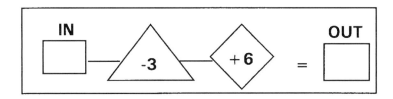

	IN	OUT
9.	7	10
10.	15	
11.	18	
12.	11	

BRAIN TICKLER

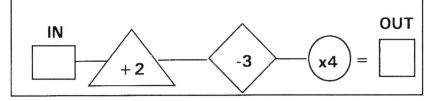

	IN	OUT
13.	3	8
14.	6	
15.	12	
16.	21	

Using logic to solve 2 and 3-step pattern equations

NAME _____

The IN-OUT Super Challenge No. 2

DIRECTIONS: Some charts have more than one step. Complete this IN-OUT chart. Use each number in the IN list. Write the answer in the OUT list. The first problem has been done for you on each IN-OUT chart.

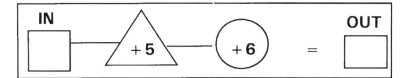

	IN	OUT
1.	9	20
2.	8	
3.	10	
4.	13	

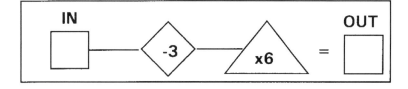

	IN	OUT
5.	4	6
6.	11	
7.	7	
8.	9	

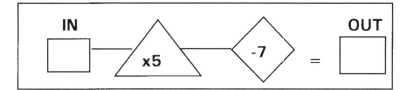

	IN	OUT
9.	3	8
10.	6	
11.	10	
12.	12	

BRAIN TICKLER

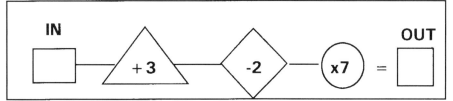

	IN	OUT
13.	5	42
14.	8	
15.	11	
16.	50	

Improving problem solving skills   NAME_____

SIMPLY A-MAZ-ING!

DIRECTIONS: To complete each maze, start at the top line and move to the bottom line. You may move vertically, diagonally, or horizontally. An example has been done for you.

EXAMPLE: Move through the maze making the total **90** by <u>multiplying</u> each number by the next.

2	4	10	3	9	5
8	3	5	8	2	10
7	6	1	5	8	4
2	9	7	6	3	9

EXAMPLE:
2 x 3 = 6, 6 x 1 = 6, 6 x 5 = 30, 30 x 3 = 90

Move through the maze making the total **64** by <u>multiplying</u> each number by the next.

2	10	4	3	9	3
4	2	6	7	8	7
9	8	1	2	10	4
5	7	9	5	1	2

5	6	3	9	4	10
8	10	6	2	8	9
9	7	7	5	1	4
4	6	8	6	7	3

Move through the maze making the total **810** by <u>multiplying</u> each number by the next.

SUPER CHALLENGE!

Move through the maze making the total **56,000** by <u>multiplying</u> each number by the next.

10	5	8	20	6	9
4	3	6	7	30	7
7	20	4	8	1	5
9	7	1	5	10	20

NAME_____

Drabbles and Narps

DIRECTIONS: Discovering how objects are alike or different can
help you improve your powers of observations. Solve the two
logic problems below.

1. **All of these are *Drabbles*.**

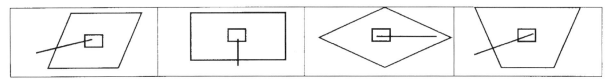

None of these are *Drabbles*.

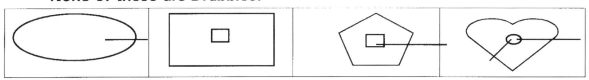

Which of these are *Drabbles*? Circle them.

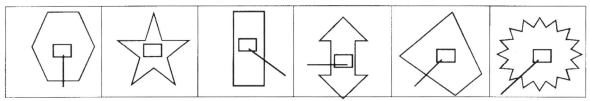

2. **All of these are *Narps*.**

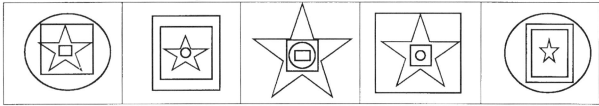

None of these are *Narps*.

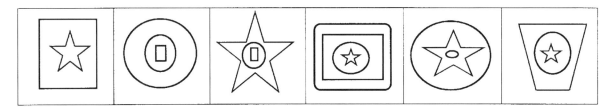

Which of these are *Narps*? Circle the *Narps*.

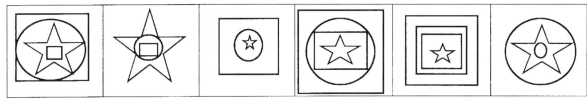

ANSWER KEY

Page 1 Answers will vary.

Page 2 Answers will vary.

Page 3 1. 4,5,1,3,6,2   2. 6,2,4,5,1,3   3. 3,2,6,4,5,1   4. 4,3,5,2,6,1   5. 4,3,2,5,6,1

Page 4 1. 6   2. 3 3. 20   4. 7   5. 5   6. 9   7. 10 (On a toadstool)

Page 5 Balloons whose answers are more than 10: cents in 3 nickels ($.15), minutes in 2 hours (120), days in June (30), cents in 3 dimes ($.30), number of legs on 2 spiders (16), number inches in a foot (12), eggs in 2 dozen (24), number of months in a year (12), total number of your toes and fingers (20), 5 + 4 + 2 = 11, number of wheels on 6 cars (24)   Balloons whose answers are less than 10: half of a dozen (6), number of planets (9), 8 less than 14 (6), number of legs on a mosquito (6), number of feet in a yard (3), 17 – 9 (8).

Page 6 Order may vary in each set of facts. 2. 1. 8 + 7 = 15   2. 7 + 8 = 15   3. 15-7 = 8   4. 15-8 = 7   3. 1. 8 + 3 = 11 2. 3 + 8 = 11   3. 11-8 = 3   4. 11-3 = 8   4. 1. 4 + 5 = 9   2. 5 + 4 = 9   3. 9-4 = 5   4. 9-5 = 4

Page 7 Some colors of the balloon will vary according to students' choices.

Page 8 Order may vary with each set of facts.   2. 4 + 6 = 10 or 6 + 4 = 10, 10-4 = 6 or 10-6 = 4   3. 3 + 6 = 9 or 6 + 3 = 9, 9-3 = 6 or 9-6 = 3, 4. 6 + 6 = 12, 12-6 = 6   5. 2 + 5 = 7 or 5 + 2 = 7, 7-5 = 2 or 7-2 = 5   6. 4 + 1 = 5 or 1 + 4 = 5, 5-1 = 4 or 5-4 = 1   7. 2 + 2 = 4, 4-2 = 2   8. 6 + 5 = 11 or 5 + 6 = 11, 11-5 = 6 or 11-6 = 5

Page 9 The route goes through the following problems: 9 + 4 = 13, 7 + 4 = 11, 6 + 7 = 13, 5 + 3 = 8, 4 + 4 = 8, 2 + 9 = 11, 8 + 0 = 8, 7 + 4 = 11, 5 + 8 = 13, 6 + 2 = 8, 4 + 9 = 13, 3 + 5 = 8, 10 + 1 = 11, 4 + 4 = 8 **Bone**

Page 10 1. 8   2. 3   3. 7   4. 6   5. 4   6. 5   Bonus 1: 47   Bonus 2: 33

Page 11 1. 4,3,5   2. 6,2,2   3. 9,3,2   4. 9,11,0   5. 9, 5,4   6. 10, 8, 6   7. 16, 22, 12   8. 38, 27, 35

Page 12 1. 14   2. 13   3. 9   4. 4   5. 13   6. 9   7. 12   8. 3   9. 6   10. 10   11. 9   12. 10   13. 11   14. 10   15. 12   16. 12   17. 12   18. 7   19. 11   20. 15   21. 7   22. 10   23. 5   24. 16   25. 8   26. 2   27. 18   28. 12   29. 8   30. 7   31. 11   32. 9   33. 12   34. 17   35. 15   36. 13   37. 4   38. 11   39. 0   40. 19   41. 6   42. 8   43. 13   44. 15   45. 5   46. 15   47. 16   48. 13   49. 6   50. 13

Page 13 Game winners will vary.

Page 14 Answers for Skip Counting by 3s: 24, 30, 36, 39, 45, 51, 54, 60, 63   Answers for Skip Counting by 5s: 35, 40, 50, 55, 60, 70, 75, 80, 90,95,105,110,115,120   Answers for Skip Counting by 4s: 28, 36, 44, 48, 56, 64, 72, 80, 88, 92

Page 15 36, 40, 44, 48, 50, 54, 58, 62, 68, 70, 74, 78, 80, 84, 88, 92, 96, 98, 102, 104, 108,112, 116, 118, 122, 126, 130,   134, 136, 140, 142, 146, 150, 152, 156, 160, 164, 168, 172, 176, 180, 184, 188, 192, 194, 198, 200, 202, 206, 210, 214, 218

Page 16 1. 11   2. 14   3. 19   4. 30   5. 38   6. 12   7. 100   8. 22   9. 4   10. 6   11. 36 (The word sixty)

Page 17 Frog

Page 18 1. Even nos. are: 98, 4, 70, 88, 2, 96   2. Even nos. are: 30, 98, 44, 26, 2   3. Even nos. are: 100, 90, 22, 56   4. Odd nos. are: 21, 15, 19, 95   5. Odd nos. are: 13, 11, 17   6. Odd nos. are: 13, 1, 7, 11, 65

Page 19 Answers will vary.

Page 20 1. 17   2. 18   3. 14   4. 15   5. 13   6. 20   7. 19   8. 17

2.
2	4	6
7	0	5
3	8	1

3.
9	5	1
2	5	8
4	5	6

4.
7	4	3
3	2	9
4	8	2

5.
2	5	6
3	4	6
8	4	1

Page 22 1. 5   2. 9   3. 8   4. 6   5. 11   6. 4   (A towel)

Page 23 1. 11   2. 3   3. 10   4. 9   5. 1   6. 14   7. 15   8. 28   9. 43   10. 13   Brain Tickler Answer = 118

Page 24 1. 6, 8, 10, 12, 14, 16, 20, 22, 24, 26   2. 9, 12, 15, 18, 24, 27, 30, 36, 39   3. 10, 15, 20, 25, 30 40, 45, 50, 60, 65   4. 22, 33,   44, 55, 77, 88, 99, 121, 132   5. 6   6. 35 is the wrong key   7. 35, 42, 49, 56, 63, 77, 84, 91   Brain tickler = 19

Page 25 1. #   2. △   3. □   4. ☺   5. ⊗   6. ⊗   7. ☺   8. □   9. ⊗   10. ☺   11. ◇   12. #   13. △   14. ☺   15. #   16. ⊗

Page 26 1. <   2. >   3. <   4. >   5. >   6. <   7. <   8. <   9. <   10. >   11. <   12. <   13. >   14. <   15. >   16. <   17. >   18. <   19. <   20. >

Page 27 1. 77   2. 45   3. 99   4. 22   5. 10   6. 20   7. 16   8. 49   9. 300   10. 37   11. 100   12. 50   (An eighteen squealer)

Page 28 1. 34   2. 47   3. 16   4. 41   5. 46   6. 86   7. 15   8. 89   9. 20   (It had an earache)

Page 29 1. 99   2. 49   3. 89   4. 65   5. 35   6. 98   7. 59   8. 68   9. 88   9. 85   (It would be a boo boo)

Page 30 1. 71   2. 65   3. 150   4. 43   5. 51   6. 126   7. 112   8. 119   9. 128   (Ready, set, hoe!)

Page 31 1. 468   2. 614   3. 1,326   4. 454   5. 1,786   6. 546   7. 861   8. 159   (A slidewalk)

Page 32 1. 89   2. 103   3. 116   4. 120   5. 136   6. 198   7. 75   8. 73   (Your name)

Page 33 1. 1,011   2. 598   3. 314   4. 1,322   5. 519   6. 549   7. 1,062   8. 1,110   9. 551   10. 939   11. 770   12. 1,350   13. 1,462   14. 195   (They're known as tooth pics)

Page 34 1. 11   2. 16   3. 13   4. 35   5. 24   6. 67   7. 63   8. 23   9. 40   10. 28   11. 87   12. 71   13. 12   (She couldn't control her pupils)

Page 35 1. 19   2. 39   3. 28   4. 54   5. 9   6. 29   7. 13   8. 18   9. 49   (The space bar)

Page 36 1. 10   2. 8   3. 22   4. 15   5. 14   6. 25   7. 32   8. 33   9. 20   (It goes ahh-choo choo)

Page 37 1. 388   2. 569   3. 739   4. 79   5. 299   (Lone-ly)

Page 38 1. 19   2. 45   3. 43   4. 42   5. 23   6. 3   7. 13   8. 49   9. 32   10. 72   (It is the word "noon").

Page 39 Fire extinguisher

Page 40 1. 85   2. 29   3. 162   4. 64   5. 39   6. 12   7. 153   8. 4   9. 109   10. 92   11. 19   12. 54   (He had the drumsticks)

Page 41 1. ☺   2. 1,361 should be 1,461   3. 1,963 should be 1,962   4.☺   5. 933 should be 943   6. ☺   7. ☺   8. ☺   9. 112 should be 102

Page 42 1. 30, 37, 44, 51, 58   2. 6, 11, 16, 21, 26   3. 28, 24, 20, 16   4. 88, 77, 66, 55, 44, 33   5. 18, 27, 36, 45, 54

Page 43 Answers will vary.

Page 44 1. 36 2. 73 3. 23 4. 47 5. 202 6. 845 7. 904 8. 526 9. 412 10. 672 (They wear boooots)

Page 45 1. 310 2. 3,206 3. 46 4. 733 5. 7,303 6. 445 7. 35 8. 3,006 9. 246 10. 2,402 11. 335 12. 422 (You are too young to smoke)

Page 46 1. 3,744 2. 1,475 3. 3,006 4. 2,085 5. 9,734 6. 4,731 7. 1,430 8. 1,586

Page 47-48 No answers.

Page 49 1. 9 2. 3 3. 4 4. 0 5. 2 6. 6 7. 733,003 8. 7,303 9. 703 10. 340,304 11. 3,433 12. 34,303 (Ten q. You're welcome)

Page 50 1. 6x4=24 or 4x6=24 2. 2x9=18 or 9x2=18 3. 6x6=36 4. 8 x 8 = 64, 8 x 6 = 48 or 6 x 8 = 48 5. 4x4=16
6. 8x9=72 or 9x8=72 7. 3x4=12 or 4x3=12 8. 7x7=49 9. 3x7=21 or 7x3=21 10. 9x6=54 or 6x9=54
11. 7x9=63 or 9x7=63 12. 9x9=81

Page 51

1.
6	2	12
1	■	2
6	4	24

2.
8	4	32
2	■	1
16	2	32

3.
5	6	30
2	■	2
10	6	60

4.
7	4	28
7	■	0
49	0	0

5.
7	3	21
6	■	2
42	1	42

6.
2	10	20
2	■	1
4	5	20

7.
4	3	12
2	■	2
8	3	24

8.
3	2	6
3	■	3
9	2	18

Page 52 Crossword Puzzle – **ACROSS** A 18 B 30 C 27 D 36 E 35 G 20 I 21 J 20 K 77 N 54 O 50 P 56 Q 44 R 24 S 12
DOWN A 16 E 33 F 70 H 72 I 28 K 72 M 40 N 54 O 55 P 50 R 22 S 18 T 45

Page 53 Students' arrays will vary.

Page 54 No answers

Page 55 1. 3 x 10 = 30 There are 30 chairs in the music room. 2. 8 x 4 or 4 x 8 = 32 Mrs. Dion gave 32 jellybeans to her students for the math lesson. 3. 6 x 5 or 5 x 6 = 30 Mom got 30 stamps at the post office. 4. 5 x 9 or 9 x 5 = 45 The bookstore received 45 Harry Potter books. Arrays constructed by students will vary.

Page 56 1. 33 2. 76 3. 26 4. 15 5. 111 6. 6 7. 108 8. 37 (Smarty pants)

Page 57 1. 24 2. 36 3. 30 4. 14 5. 12 (The ice)

Page 58 1. 68 2. 69 3. 147 4. 99 5. 305 6. 208 7. 639 8. 328 (Chop them up)

Page 59 1. 574 2. 297 3. 100 4. 288 5. 415 6. 456 7. 196 8. 552 (Jellybeans)

Page 60 1. 378 2. 175 3. 144 4. 592 5. 372 6. 360 7. 387 8. 42 9. 78 10. 392 11. 200 12. 224 (The chef forgot the tomato paste)

Page 61 1. 325 2. 1,896 3. 4,104 4. 315 5. 576 6. 684 7. 1,752 8. 762 9. 280 10. 132 11. 2,691 12. 728 (Because they are bee students)

Page 62 1. 2,210 2. 2,175 3. 273 4. 4,806 5. 2,001 6. 5,544 7. 3,780 (Go to sweep)

Page 63 1. 4 x 8 = 32, 8 x 4 = 32, 32÷4 = 8, 32 ÷ 8 = 4; 2. 9 x 7 = 63, 7 x 9 = 63, 63 ÷ 9 = 7, 63 ÷ 7 = 9; 3. 6 x 8 = 48, 8 x 6 = 48, 48 ÷ 6 = 8, 48 ÷ 8 = 6, 4. 7 x 8 = 56, 8 x 7 = 56, 56 ÷ 7 = 8, 56 ÷ 8= 7

Page 64 1. 8 2. 10 3. 12 4. 7 5. 13 6. 19 7. 14 8. 11 (He eats the dentist)

Page 65 1. 22 2. 14 3. 12 4. 13 5. 43 6. 17 7. 36 8. 18 9. 25 (Springtime)

Page 66 No answers.

Page 67 1. 18 2. 37 3. 35 4. 15 5. 13 6. 7 7. 28 (Leap years)

Page 68 1. 67 2. 55 3. 63 4. 22 5. 24 6. 59 (An echo)

Page 69 1. 6 2. 21 3. 4 4. 5 5. 23 6. 27 (The Letter M)

Page 70 1. 2 2. 8 3. 13 4. 21 5. 8 6. 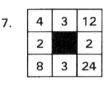 7.

Page 71

1.
In	Out	In	Out
6	12	22	28
9	15	31	37
11	17	45	51
20	26	68	74

The rule is + 6.

2.
In	Out	In	Out
10	2	30	22
12	4	36	28
16	8	50	42
24	16	10	2

The rule is –8.

3.
In	Out	In	Out
20	10	44	34
32	22	67	57
12	2	85	75

The rule is –10.

4.
In	Out	In	Out
3	9	4	12
5	15	8	24
100	300	50	150

The rule is x3

Page 72

1.

In	Out	In	Out
8	4	21	17
7	3	26	20
12	8	34	30
18	14	60	56

The rule is −4

2.

In	Out	In	Out
10	4	26	20
12	6	33	27
16	10	45	39
20	14	66	60

The rule is −6

3.

In	Out	In	Out
2	4	11	22
5	10	13	26
6	12	25	50

The rule is x2.

4.

In	Out	In	Out
15	5	33	11
21	7	45	15
30	10	99	33

The rule is ÷3

Page 73

1	2	3	4
2	1	4	3
3	4	1	2
4	3	2	1

This is one possible solution.

Page 74 1. ant 2. boa 3. bat 4. frog 5. eagle 6. rat 1. hot dog 2. tomato 3. cookie 4. fries 5. steak 6. ice cream

Page 75 1. 27 2. 56 3. 74 4. 47 5. 54 6. 29 7. 17 8. 88 9. 55

Page 76 1. 48 2. 44 3, 33 4. 7 5. 86 6. 38 7. 67 8. 2 9. 51 10. 66 11. 24 (In the dictionary)

Page 78 1. 68 ft. 2. 300 legs 3. 2014 4. 1,540 lbs. 5. 200 miles 6. 225 sharks (Monopoly)

Page 79 1. 220 years 2. 3,500 ants 3. 2009 4. 25 hours 5. 24 bicycles 6. 300,000 lbs. 7. 60 buckets
8. 28 legs 9. 24,500 eggs (Made a web site)

Page 80 1. 32 squares 2. If the chart of numbers is turned upside down, the numbers can still add up to the same answer in each row, column, and diagonal.

Page 81 Some of the solutions are: 1. 3 + 4 + 6 + 2 = 15, 2. 3 + 6 + 2 + 4 = 15
3. 3 + 2 + 4 + 6 = 15, 4. 3 + 4 + 2 + 6 = 15, 5. 4 + 3 + 6 + 2 = 15 6. 4 + 6 + 3 + 2 = 15 7. 4 + 2 + 3 + 6 = 15
8. 4 + 2 + 6 + 3 = 15 9. 3 + 4 + 6 + 2 = 15 10. 3 + 6 + 2 + 4 = 15 11. 3 + 2 + 6 + 4 = 15 12. 3 + 4 + 2 + 6 = 15

Page 82 1. 40 = 5 + 15 + 20 = 40 2. 33 = 20 + 8 + 5 = 33 3. 60 = 35 + 2 + 8 + 15 4. 42 = 25 + 15 + 2
5. 65 = 35 + 20 + 2 + 8 6. 70 = 8 + 35 + 2 + 20 + 5 7. 38 = 5 + 8 + 25 8. 100 = 35 + 25 + 20 + 15 + 5
9. 15 = 8 + 5 + 2 10. 45 = 8 + 35 + 2

Page 83 1. 8 x 8 = 64 64 ÷ 2 = 32 32 − 2 = 30 2. 6 x 9 = 54 54 ÷ 2 = 27 27 + 3 = 30 3. 9 x 3 = 27 27 − 2 = 25
25 + 5 = 30 4. 7 x 4 = 28 28 − 6 = 22 22 + 8 = 30 5. 9 x 3 = 27 27 − 5 = 22 22 + 8 = 30 6. 5 x 5 = 25
25 ÷ 5 = 5 5 x 6 = 30

Page 84

	IN	OUT
1.	6	13
2.	2	9
3.	5	12
4.	7	14

	IN	OUT
5.	5	8
6.	10	13
7.	12	15
8.	4	7

	IN	OUT
9.	7	10
10.	15	18
11.	18	21
12.	11	14

	IN	OUT
13.	3	8
14.	6	20
15.	12	44
16.	21	80

Page 85

	IN	OUT
1.	9	21
2.	8	19
3.	10	21
4.	13	24

	IN	OUT
5.	4	6
6.	11	48
7.	7	24
8.	8	36

	IN	OUT
9.	3	8
10.	6	23
11.	10	43
12.	12	53

	IN	OUT
13.	5	42
14.	8	63
15.	11	84
16.	50	357

Page 86

1.

2	4	10	3	9	5
8	3	5	8	2	10
7	6	1	5	8	4
2	9	7	6	1	9

90

2.

2	10	4	3	9	3
4	2	6	7	8	7
9	8	1	2	10	4
5	7	9	5	1	2

64

3.

5	6	3	9	4	10
8	10	6	2	8	9
9	7	7	5	1	4
4	6	8	6	7	3

810

4.

10	5	8	20	6	9
4	3	6	2	30	7
7	20	4	8	1	5
9	7	1	5	10	20

56,000

Page 87

1.

These are *Drabbles*. All *Drabbles* have four sides, a rectangle in the center of the four-sided figure, and a straight line coming from or to the rectangle.

2.

These are *Nards*. All *Nards* have 2 rectangles, a circle, and a star.